Professional Diploma Synoptic

Workbook

Celia Laverick

Published by Osborne Books Limited
Tel 01905 748071
Email books@osbornebooks.co.uk
Website www.osbornebooks.co.uk

Design by Laura Ingham

Printed by CPI Group (UK) Limited, Croydon, CR0 4YY, on environmentally friendly, acid-free paper from managed forests.

British Library Cataloguing in Publication Data
A catalogue record for this book is available from the British Library

ISBN 978 1911 198 093

Contents

Introduction

Qualifications covered

This book has been written specifically to cover the AAT Synoptic Assessment, which is mandatory for the following qualifications:

AAT Professional Diploma in Accounting – Level 4

AAT Professional Diploma in Accounting at SCQF Level 8

This book provides four full Practice Assessments (with answers) to prepare the student for the Computer Based Synoptic Assessments. Further details of the content and structure of the book are shown on page 1.

Osborne Study and Revision Materials

The materials featured on the previous page are tailored to the needs of students studying this Unit and revising for the assessment. They include:

- **Tutorials:** paperback books with practice activities
- **Student Zone:** access to Osborne Books online resources
- **Osborne Books App:** Osborne Books ebooks for mobiles and tablets

Visit www.osbornebooks.co.uk for details of study and revision resources and access to online material.

HOW TO USE THIS SYNOPTIC ASSESSMENT WORKBOOK

INTRODUCTION

The AAT Professional Diploma in Accounting covers high-level accounting and finance topics and tasks. It includes a wide range of financial management skills and applications; drafting financial statements for limited companies; recommending accounting systems strategy; and constructing and presenting complex management accounting reports. It also covers specialist areas such as tax, auditing, credit management, and cash and treasury management.

This qualification comprises four mandatory units and two specialist units selected from a choice of five options. The mandatory units are:

- Management Accounting: Budgeting*
- Management Accounting: Decision and Control*
- Financial Statements of Limited Companies*
- Accounting Systems and Controls

The optional units are:

- Business Tax
- Personal Tax
- External Auditing
- Cash and Treasury Management
- Credit Management

Three of the mandatory units are assessed individually in end-of-unit assessments (in the bulleted list above these are indicated with a *). This qualification also includes a synoptic assessment that students sit towards the end of the qualification, which draws on and assesses knowledge and understanding from across all four of the mandatory units in the qualification.

All of the optional units are assessed individually in end-of-unit assessments and students will sit assessments for the two optional units that they select. These optional units do not form part of the synoptic assessment.

Students must successfully complete all three of the unit assessments for the mandatory units, two optional unit assessments and the synoptic assessment to achieve the qualification.

SYNOPTIC ASSESSMENT COVERAGE

One unit in this qualification is only assessed through the synoptic assessment, 'Accounting Systems and Control.' However, the synoptic assessment for the Professional Diploma in Accounting covers all four of the mandatory units and has six assessment objectives. These are detailed below:

AO1 Demonstrate an understanding of the roles and responsibilities of the accounting function within an organisation and examine ways of preventing and detecting fraud and systemic weaknesses.

AO2 Evaluate budgetary reporting and its effectiveness in controlling and improving organisational performance.

AO3 Evaluate an organisation's accounting control systems and procedures.

AO4 Analyse an organisation's decision making and control using management accounting tools.

AO5 Analyse an organisation's decision making and control using ratio analysis.

AO6 Analyse the internal controls of an organisation and make recommendations.

SYNOPTIC ASSESSMENT STRUCTURE

The synoptic assessment for the Professional Diploma in Accounting is a computer based assessment that is partially computer marked and partially human-marked. The live synoptic assessment is three hours long.

Students are provided with pre-release material that is made available to them ahead of their assessment. This material is designed to contextualise the tasks in the sample assessment. Studying this material will encourage students to think about the assessment topics in an integrated way, which is necessary for performing well in the synoptic assessment.

Students will not be able to take a copy of the pre-release material into the assessment. However, access to this material will be available through pop-up windows in the assessment. All live assessments will be based on a single piece of pre-release material.

WHAT THIS BOOKS CONTAINS

This book provides four full Practice Synoptic Assessments to prepare the student for the live Computer Based Assessments. They are based directly on the structure, style and content of the sample assessment material provided by the AAT at www.aat.org.uk.

Each of the four practice assessments is based on a different company and the pre-release material will be unique to each practice assessment. This will provide students a good idea of the types of scenarios that could form the basis of the live assessment.

It is suggested that students should read the pre-release material before they attempt the practice assessment in the same way as they will when they sit their live assessment.

The AAT sample assessment material provides a breakdown of the marks allocated to each task. This helps students to appreciate the relative importance of each task in the assessment and to plan how long to spend on each task. The Practice Synoptic Assessments in this book also show the mark allocation for each task.

Suggested answers to the Practice Assessments are set out in this book.

The AAT recommend that students complete all other assessments before attempting the synoptic assessment and there are restrictions in place to prevent premature scheduling of the synoptic assessment. It is suggested that in order to gain maximum benefit from this book students should not attempt these Practice Synoptic Assessments until they have studied all four mandatory units and completed the three unit assessments.

Practice synoptic assessment 1

Pre-release material

Company background and history

Adams and Blackwall Ltd (ABL) is a heating servicing and maintenance company operating throughout the West Country.

The company is run from a head office on an industrial estate in Exeter and from 7 branches throughout the region.

ABL was established in the early 1990s by two of its current directors, James Adams and Hazel Adams (Nee Blackwall). James and Hazel are majority shareholders. Shares are also held by the other directors and key employees who are encouraged to acquire them through an employee share scheme.

Starting with a single branch in Exeter, the company has grown organically, gradually establishing its branch network throughout the region.

In 20-5 the company had revenue of £22 million and employed 370FTE employees, 280 of whom were qualified engineers, the rest trainees, site support and office staff. In 20-5 ABL won a contract which involved significant work in the Barnstaple area. This has initially been covered by other branches, but the opening of a branch in Barnstaple was agreed for January 20-6, both to expand the business and to ensure the profitability of the contract.

Mission statement

To be the best heating servicing and maintenance company in the region.

We aim to provide the highest possible level of service to clients, completing installations on time and attending call-outs as speedily as possible, always treating clients with courtesy and respect.

We operate to high ethical standards and aim to promote sustainability both with clients and through the way we do business.

Developments in the market

The dismantling of council housing and council in-house maintenance which started in the 1980s is ongoing. Cuts in council budgets and growth in housing associations providing social housing have led to growth in the industry. However competition is keen and margins on tenders can be very tight.

Renewable energy systems have been very much in demand. ABL has invested in MCS accreditation (an industry standard "Microgeneration Certification Scheme"), and also in staff training in order to be able to compete in this new sector of the market and has seen promising growth in this area. However, recent government cuts in subsidies for renewables make this sector of the market less certain.

Strategic planning

Long-term success is felt to be dependent on both successful retendering to existing clients as well as winning new long-term clients. The company uses the 'balanced scorecard' to assess its overall performance:

Learning and growth

Staff retention is good.

Staff development and progression – ABL runs an apprenticeship scheme which commonly leads to qualification and employment as an engineer. In 20-5 eight engineers were promoted to senior engineers and the Exeter Senior Engineer was promoted to Operations Director taking over this role from James Adams who had previously combined this role with that of Managing Director. All engineers are on the Gas Safe Register and 25% have now completed MCS training (up from 20% in 20-4).

Business processes

The efficiency of a servicing engineer is measured in terms of average call outs per week. This declines when engineers are covering a wide area and need to spend significant amounts of time travelling. The establishment of a new branch at Barnstaple should improve efficiency.

In 20-5, speed limiters were introduced to company vans for all branches other than Exeter (where travel is mainly around the city). This has helped to cut fuel costs.

Customers

During 20-5 ABL lost 2% of its long-term clients in retendering. They gained several new clients during the year and their overall client base has grown by 3% over 20-5. Several housing associations have been through periods of growth and ABL has benefited from this growth.

Financial

Revenue grew by 11% in 20-5. The gross profit margin remained fairly stable despite downward pressure on bid prices tendered. Dividends paid to shareholders grew in proportion to sales growth. ABL is funded largely by retained earnings.

Strategic mapping

Management believe that continued focus both on staff development and staff progression in the firm will ensure the continued success of the business. Expansion of the branch network to increase business efficiency gives additional opportunities for staff to be promoted to more senior roles within the firm. In addition, the expansion should enable better customer service and improve customer retention. Expansion of staff capabilities with regard to the installation and maintenance of renewable energy systems will also be a basis for future growth.

Staff

ABL's key staff are as follows:

Managing Director (MD)	James Adams
Operations Director (OD)	Philip Evans
Sales Director (SD)	Ruby Wentworth
Finance Director (FD)	Richard Johns
Human Resources Director (HRD)	Hazel Adams

All branch managers report to the Operations Director as do the senior engineers.

The FD heads up the Accounts Department which includes a Management Accountant who is responsible for budgeting and costing activities and a Financial Accountant who is responsible for producing statutory accounts and returns and overseeing the work of the accounts clerks. There are four accounts clerks – a Payroll Clerk, Purchase Ledger Clerk (Accounts Payable Clerk), Sales Ledger Clerk (Accounts Receivable Clerk) and an Accounts Assistant.

ABL's financial statements

ABL Statement of profit or loss for the year ended 31.12.20-5

Continuing operations	*£000*
Revenue	22,500
Cost of sales	19,100
Gross profit	3,400
Operating expenses	2,320
Operating profit	1,080
Finance costs	40
Profit before tax	1,040
Tax	240
Profit for the period from continuing operations	800

ABL Statement of financial position as at 31.12.20-5

	£000
Assets	
Non-Current assets	
Plant property and equipment	625
Current assets	
Inventories	1,075
Trade receivables	4,610
Cash and cash equivalents	690
	7,000
Equities and liabilities	
Ordinary share capital (£1 shares)	480
Retained earnings	3,620
Non-current liabilities	
Loans	500
Current liabilities	
Trade payables	2,200
Taxation	200
	7,000

TASKS

Task 1: 20 marks

Multiple choice questions on the topics of roles and responsibilities of the accounting function, preventing and detecting frauds, and ethics.

(a) Management accounts are produced for more than one reason. Which of the reasons given below are valid justifications for the production of management accounts.

Reason	Valid	Not valid
(a) To monitor current costs against budget		
(b) To comply with International Accounting Standards		
(c) To monitor liquidity		
(d) To detect fraud		
(e) To comply with statutory obligations to report results		

(5 marks)

(b) The Accounts Assistant uses completed job cards to prepare sales invoices for maintenance work. These list details of: the engineer who carried out the work, details of the work done and of the parts which were used. The Accounts Assistant discovers that one job card has not been signed by the customer on completion of the work.

What is the correct action for the Accounts Assistant to take?

(a) Prepare the sales invoice as normal	
(b) Prepare the sales invoice as normal, but also keep a copy of the job card and send the original back to the relevant Branch Manager for investigation	
(c) Prepare the sales invoice as normal, but also keep a copy of the job card and send the original back to the relevant Engineer for investigation	

(3 marks)

(c) The Purchase Ledger Clerk (Accounts Payable Clerk), asks you to state whether the following errors and omissions would be detected by reconciling suppliers' statements to the supplier's purchase ledger account (Accounts payable ledger account).

Error/Omission	**Would be detected**	**Would not be detected**
(a) A purchase invoice is omitted from a supplier's account		
(b) A purchase invoice is posted to the wrong supplier's account		
(c) A supplier sends in an invoice for goods/services which were not received		
(d) The supplier's invoice charges higher amounts than agreed		
(e) An inputting error is made when recording the amount of a purchase invoice		

(5 marks)

(d) The Purchase Ledger Clerk (Accounts Payable Clerk) receives an email from a large supplier. The email says that the supplier has changed its bank account details and requests that future payments be made to a new bank account.

What actions should the Purchase Ledger Clerk take?

(a) Check that the email is from a valid email address from the supplier in question	
(b) Ask for a letter on supplier headed paper signed by a known signatory confirming the request	
(c) Call the supplier by phone to confirm the details	
(d) Get authorisation for the change from the Financial Accountant	
(e) All of the above	

(2 marks)

(e) The Financial Accountant takes a call from a prospective customer who asks whether it might be possible for him to pay for an installation in advance, and then cancel and get a refund should the quote be unsatisfactory. The Financial Accountant considers this request to be suspicious and is concerned that the proposed transaction might be money laundering.

(1) Which **two** of the Financial Accountant's fundamental principles are most affected in this situation?

Select two from:

- Professional behaviour
- Professional competence and due care
- Confidentiality
- Integrity
- Objectivity

(3 marks)

(2) To whom should money laundering suspicions be reported? Tick **one** choice.

(a) The Money Laundering Reporting Officer	
(b) The National Crime Agency	
(c) The AAT	
(d) The Financial Reporting Council	

(2 marks)

Task 2: 15 marks

Evaluating budgetary reporting

The decision to open a branch at Barnstaple was made late December 20-5 with the location of a suitable site. One of the deputy branch managers along with a couple of engineers were approached at that point and they agreed to set up and run the new branch. Budgets for 20-6 for all the other branches had already been set at this date so the Finance Officer asked the Management Accountant to produce a budget for the new branch based on discussions with the OD, and the SD.

The figures, which were hastily produced include:

- Sales based on 200% of existing contracts
- Staff costs of 38% of revenue in line with the Exeter branch
- Fuel and operating costs all estimated at the same percentage of revenue as applies to the Exeter branch

You are required to:

(a) Explain the assumptions and limitations of the budgeted figures. (3 marks)

(b) Explain whether the Barnstaple manager will be motivated to try to achieve his budget. (2 marks)

(c) Explain whether the use of standard costing techniques would help with the preparation of a more realistic and challenging budget. (4 marks)

(d) Explain if the use of rolling budgets might help in the management of the Barnstaple branch during its first year. (4 marks)

(e) Suggest **two** performance measures which could be used to monitor performance at the Barnstaple branch. (2 marks)

Task 3: 15 marks

Evaluating systems and procedures

You have been asked to carry out a review of ABL's payroll procedures which are outlined below.

Branches use a job costing software package called Userve to record and manage jobs that engineers attend. Recording starts with a quote and progresses as actual costs are reported. The overall profitability of individual jobs are monitored both at the branch and by Head Office.

At each branch, engineers submit weekly timesheets to Branch Managers who check information to Userve before signing timesheets to approve them and passing them to a branch clerk for input to Userve. Timesheets are then filed at the branch. Hours recorded are picked up from Userve and input into the payroll software at head office by the Payroll Clerk.

Branch office staff are required to complete weekly timesheets which are signed by branch managers before being scanned and emailed to head office where details are input into the payroll software by the Payroll Clerk.

Recruitment of new staff is normally managed by HR at head office, but occasionally a branch manager will employ an additional member of staff on a temporary basis. This is not considered a problem as it mainly relates to cleaners or to engineers required to cover staff sickness on an emergency basis.

The company uses "Sage Payroll" to perform all payroll processing. The Payroll Clerk is fully trained in this system and the Financial Accountant has completed basic training in it. Access to the system is password protected, the Payroll Clerk has full user rights and the Financial Accountant has administrator rights.

The Payroll Clerk is responsible for inputting all timesheets received before the 25th of each month onto the system and for running the monthly payroll. Employees are paid by BACS on the last working day of the month.

Payroll prints along with the BACS payment authority are produced by the Payroll Clerk and passed to the Financial Accountant for approval. The Financial Accountant checks that the payroll prints agree to the BACS schedule and that amounts in total are in line with the previous month, significant discrepancies are investigated.

Back-up copies of payroll data are stored on site in a fireproof safe.

Identify FIVE systemic weaknesses in ABL's internal controls for handling payroll. Explain how each weakness which you have identified could create a problem for the company.

Weakness	Potential problem for the company

Task 4: 15 marks

Analyse decision making and control using management accounting tools

Part 1

Management at ABL are assessing the number of engineers who should be based at Barnstaple.

Fixed costs for January 20-6 at Barnstaple are estimated to be £15,400.

Engineers' work earns an average contribution of £10 per hour.

Engineers work on average 140 chargeable hours per month.

The Barnstaple manager thinks that he will be able to deploy 13 engineers during January.

(a) Calculate how many engineers should be based at Barnstaple in January for the branch to break-even.

(2 marks)

(b) What percentage margin of safety does the Barnstaple branch have for January to two decimal places?

(2 marks)

Head office fixed costs are allocated and apportioned to branches. Management confirms a recharge of £5,000 to Barnstaple for January (in addition to the £15,400 site costs).

(c) Explain whether or not the Barnstaple site is still viable for January.

(2 marks)

Part 2

One of ABL's main costs is that of vans. Each engineer needs a van to complete his or her work. New vans cost approximately £11,000 and are used for four years before being sold for £3,800 approx.

The company is considering the option of leasing the vans for four years at a cost of £1,900 per annum payable in advance. Service and maintenance costs are not included.

(a) Calculate the net present cost of the purchase of a van for £11,000 with a trade in value of £3,800 at the end of four years. Show costs as positive and revenues as negative.

(3 marks)

Time	0	1	2	3	4
Investment (scrap)					
Discount factor 8%	1	0.926	0.857	0.794	0.735
Present value					
Net present cost					

(b) Calculate the net present cost of the lease of a van for £1,900 paid in advance for four years.

(3 marks)

Time	**0**	**1**	**2**	**3**	**4**
Lease payment					
Discount factor 8%	1	0.926	0.857	0.794	0.735
Present value					
Net present cost					

(c) Recommend whether or not the van should be bought or leased on financial grounds.

(1 mark)

Another option offered by the leasing company is to pay a higher lease payment which includes maintenance costs as part of the lease. If ABL took this option they could replace branch mechanics who are currently responsible for this work with less skilled staff who would only need to clean the vans.

(d) Explain the risks arising to the business of choosing this policy.

(2 marks)

Task 5: 20 marks

Calculation of ratios and selection of appropriate comments

(a) Use the financial statements shown to complete the calculation of financial ratios shown below.

(10 marks)

ABL Statement of profit or loss

	Year ended 31.12.20-4	Year ended 31.12.20-5
	£000	*£000*
Revenue	20,250	22,500
Gross profit	3,139	3,400
Operating profit	931	1,080
ABL Statement of financial position		
Assets		
Non-Current assets	650	625
Inventories	970	1,075
Trade receivables	4,327	4,610
Cash and cash equivalents	553	690
	6,500	7,000
Equities and liabilities		
Equity	3,718	4,100
Non-current liabilities	500	500
Trade payables	2,110	2,200
Taxation	172	200
	6,500	7,000

Ratios

Show profitability, financial position and liquidity ratios to two decimal places. Working capital ratios should be rounded to the nearest day.

Ratio	Year ended 31.12.20-4	Year ended 31.12.20-5
Profitability		
Gross profit margin %	15.50%	15.11%
Operating profit margin %	4.60%	4.80%
Return on capital employed	22.07%	
Financial position		
Gearing	11.85%	
Liquidity		
Quick/acid test ratio	2.14:1	
Working capital management		
Inventory holding period	21 days	
Trade receivables collection period	78 days	75 days
Trade payables payment period	45 days	42 days
Working capital cycle	54 days	

(b) Complete the commentary on ABL's results below giving numerical answers to two decimal places.

(10 Marks)

Profitability

Revenue has grown by [ ] %. The gross profit margin has decreased by [ ] %. The cause of this difference is the low margins on some of the installations successfully tendered for.

The level of growth in the operating profit margin indicates **good/poor** (delete as appropriate) control over overheads.

Financial position

ABL continues to have **high/medium/low** *(delete as appropriate)* levels of gearing.

Liquidity

ABL has **high/low** *(delete as appropriate)* levels of liquidity and could be considered to be **overtrading/overcapitalised**. *(delete as appropriate)*

Working capital management

The components of the working capital cycle are fairly constant. The trade receivables collection period has **improved/deteriorated** *(delete as appropriate)* slightly and the trade payables payment period has **improved/deteriorated** *(delete as appropriate)* a little.

Overall performance

The **growth/decline** *(delete as appropriate)* in the return on capital employed indicates an overall **improvement/decline** *(delete as appropriate)* in performance.

Task 6: 15 marks

Analyse internal controls and make recommendations

You have been asked to review ABLs purchasing procedures and to make recommendations for improvement.

Procedures are as follows:

Capital expenditure

ABL's Purchasing Manager is responsible for negotiating all new orders for capital items such as vehicles and equipment. Orders over the value of £1,000 need to be countersigned by one of the directors. The company has a purchase order module in its accounting software which automatically numbers all orders issued and which allows deliveries to be matched against purchase orders by stores and then transmitted to the Purchase Ledger Clerk who matches the received orders against invoices, checks them and passes them for payment.

Plumbing and heating systems and supplies, including microgeneration systems

Parts are ordered by branches on the direction of the Branch Manager as advised by engineers. They are charged against the relevant jobs on Userve. Userve does not have a purchase order module but the Purchase Ledger Clerk at head office who receives the invoices can check them against quoted prices recorded on Userve. Branches have built up good relationships with local suppliers over the years and will order from them.

Fuel

The company has an account with BP. Engineers can fill up vans at BP garages and sign for the fuel on the head office account. BP garages use a number plate recognition system so only company vehicles can be refuelled. Head office are sent monthly bills by BP along with a detailed breakdown of fuel usage by vehicle which is used to monitor mileage costs.

Utilities and office supplies

ABL's Purchasing Manager is responsible for negotiating all remaining revenue items using the purchase order system for capital expenditure.

(a) Identify one strength in the procedures. Explain how the business benefits from this.

(b) Identify one weakness in these procedures. Explain how this damages the business and suggest a remedy.

(c) Identify an opportunity to improve the procedures. Explain how the procedure should be changed and how the business could benefit.

(d) Identify one threat to the effectiveness of these procedures. Explain how this could damage the business and suggest an action that would reduce the risk.

Practice synoptic assessment 2

Pre-release material

Company background and history

CD Malt Ltd (CDM) is a manufacturer of malted grains and malted products mainly for sale to the brewing industry in the UK. Originally founded in Victorian times, as a small Lincolnshire firm selling purely to brewers in Lincoln, it grew over the years and subsequently merged with a Southampton based operation. Then in the 1990s it was bought by an American conglomerate. The US-based parent company has recently experienced financial problems which have led to a decision in the last year to look for a buyer for CDM. In consequence, the UK directors of the malt business raised the finance necessary for a management buyout of the business which went through at the end of the last financial year.

CDM is run from an industrial site in Lincolnshire close to the area in which the grains are grown, with a second manufacturing facility in Southampton. The Lincolnshire site accounts for approximately 2/3 of its production of malted products each year. The firm's business is seasonal in that grains need to be purchased at, or shortly after, harvest and then stored until required for production, with consequent impacts on cash flow.

Provisional figures for the annual accounts for the year just ended show revenue of £25 million and a profit for the year of £0.8 million. The company employs 120 FTE employees, 100 of whom work in production and delivery, the remainder in administration.

Mission statement

To obtain the best quality grains and use them to produce the best quality malt and malted products and to provide our customers with the highest standards of service.

We aim to benefit shareholders, staff and the communities in which we work, operating ethically and sustainably.

Developments in the market

Beer sales in the UK have been in decline for many years resulting in reducing demand. The company has a limited range of products and so has maintained sales by moving into the market for micro-breweries and craft breweries. This has been augmented by increased sales of malt to the EU and to developing economies such as India and Thailand. The market for whisky remains strong and long-term growth is predicted in the production of malts for distilling.

Strategic planning

As part of the management buyout process, the managers assessed the underlying business using the balanced scorecard – which is shown below updated for the recent draft financial results:

Learning and growth

CDM focuses on this perspective in three ways, firstly, staff on its product development team are experienced, well qualified and committed. Secondly, the firm is committed to staff training and development and staff at all levels are encouraged to undertake relevant training; this is combined with recruitment processes which ensure high calibre new employees. Thirdly, the firm is committed to opening channels of communication from "shop floor" employees to management to ensure that insights from those carrying out the work are fed into company developments.

Business processes

In the last two years, the Lincolnshire production site benefitted from the updating and upgrading of production facilities improving its capacity to produce the finest grade malts of a consistent quality and improving its carbon foot print at the same time through improved heat reclamation in the drying process (kilning). The production facility at Southampton is in need of similar levels of investment to improve production quality and consistency. Production has quality accreditations including ISO9001 and Assured UK Malt (AUKM).

Customers

Customers range from multi-national breweries who buy malt by the tonne, to small micro-breweries who buy 25kg sacks of malt. CDM works hard to know its customers and to provide a high standard of service, and as a result it has a stable customer base. Sales have grown by 4% over the last year and customer satisfaction surveys have provided positive feedback.

Financial

Revenue growth combined with improved efficiencies at the firm's largest production site have combined to bring a 20% increase to the firm's operating profit. The firm's Return on Capital Employed is 13.5%, up from 12.1% a year ago. The biggest challenge faced from the financial perspective relates to funding. The directors have financed the management buyout by borrowings and it is unlikely that they will be able to obtain significant amounts of additional finance in the short term.

Management focus

Despite the strong position illustrated by the balanced scorecard, the firm faces many challenges in the short-term as it begins to operate independently. The conglomerate had operated as a number of divisions with sales and production having separate reporting lines across the group. Management reporting structures need to be redeveloped to suit CDM as a single entity. In addition CDM has been using systems software developed to suit the group and it is now in the process of implementing the installation of new software across all areas of operations. The implementation outline is as follows:

Month 1: Administration, General ledger, invoicing and Sales ledger

Month 2: Purchase ledger, Human resources (and payroll), Inventory

Month 3: Manufacturing, Sales order processing, Purchase order processing

Staff

CD Malt's shareholders and directors are:

Managing Director (MD)	Simon Grainger
Production Director (PD)	Paul Arnold
Sales Director (SD)	Deborah Jones
Finance Director (FD)	Oliver Matthews
Human Resources Director (HRD)	Jayne McDonald

The Southampton site is run by its Production Manager, Mark Widacombe.

The FD is in charge of the treasury aspects of the firm, including negotiating loans and forward contracts to protect the company from commodity price fluctuations as well as fluctuations in foreign exchange rates. He is also in charge of the Accounts Department which is made up of seven staff consisting of a Management Accountant who is responsible for budgeting and costing as well as ad hoc analysis and reports, and a Financial Accountant responsible for the production of the annual statutory accounts as well as the monthly management accounts and for overseeing transaction processing. Transaction processing is carried out by: the Assistant Accountant responsible for credit control, VAT returns and monitoring the bank account and month end adjustments, the Sales Ledger Clerk (Accounts Receivable Clerk), Purchase Ledger Clerk(Accounts Payable Clerk), Payroll Clerk and the temporary Accounts Assistant.

CD Malt's financial statements

CD Malt Statement of profit or loss for the year ended 31.12.20-6

Continuing operations	*£000*
Revenue	25,124
Cost of sales	19,597
Gross profit	5,527
Operating expenses	3,248
Operating profit	2,279
Finance costs	1,294
Profit before tax	985
Tax	216
Profit for the period from continuing operations	769

CD Malt Statement of financial position as at 31.12.20-6

	£000
Assets	
Non-Current assets	
Plant property and equipment	13,444
Current assets	
Inventories	6,127
Trade receivables	3,411
Cash and cash equivalents	23
	23,005
Equities and liabilities	
Ordinary share capital (£1 shares)	300
Retained earnings	6,472
Non-current liabilities	
Debenture loans	9,200
Pension liabilities	950
Current liabilities	
Trade payables	5,966
Taxation	117
	23,005

TASKS

Task 1: 20 marks

Multiple choice questions on the topics of roles and responsibilities of the accounting function, preventing and detecting frauds, and ethics.

(a) Now that CD Malt is operating as an independent company, what regulations will need to be followed when it prepares its year-end accounts? Tick all that apply.

Regulation	Apply
(a) Companies Act 2006	
(b) Sarbanes–Oxley (2002)	
(c) London Stock Exchange regulations	
(d) Accounting standards	
(e) Financial Conduct Authority regulations	

(4 marks)

(b) The Accounts Assistant has been employed on a temporary basis to help assist with transaction processing during the transition to the new IT systems. Before completing any tasks the Accounts Assistant is required to read the procedure notes for that task and is then monitored by the relevant clerk. These arrangements demonstrate:

(a) Strong system controls	
(b) Good segregation of duties	
(c) Strong physical controls	
(d) A good control environment	

(2 marks)

(c) Mark Widacombe, the Southampton Manager, phones to report that a member of staff has left. Who would be the most appropriate person for him to talk to?

(a) The Payroll Clerk	
(b) The Financial Accountant	
(c) The Finance Director	
(d) The Human Resources Director	

(2 marks)

(d) The Accounts Assistant has reconciled the money in the petty cash tin, together with the vouchers, to the float amount at the start of the month and found a shortfall. State whether the following problems could have caused the shortage.

Problem	**Could have caused shortage**	**Would not cause shortage**
(a) Miscoding of petty cash voucher as travel rather than subsistence		
(b) Theft of money from the petty cash tin		
(c) Petty cash claims have been paid for more than the maximum amount allowed		
(d) Addition error on petty cash voucher		
(e) Clerical error paying out the wrong amount of petty cash		

(5 marks)

(e) Which of the following IT system controls helps to protect accounting data from:

(1) Human error

(2) Power failure

	Human error	Power failure
(a) Audit trails showing all transactions posted and who posted them		
(b) Individual user-names and passwords for all users		
(c) Automatic back-ups		
(d) A firewall which filters incoming email and destroys suspect items		
(e) Sense checks which do not allow the posting of transactions with dates outside the current period		

(5 marks)

(f) The whole accounts team are extremely busy during period 1 with the introduction of the new IT systems for the General ledger and Sales ledger.

Which **one** of the fundamental accounting principles is most threatened by this situation?

(Select one from: Professional Behaviour, professional competence and due care, confidentiality, integrity and objectivity.)

(2 marks)

Task 2: 15 marks

Evaluating budgetary reporting.

CDM need to produce monthly management accounts and have decided that they want to include a budgetary control report as part of this. The following is a draft budgetary control report produced for period 12 of last year.

Lincolnshire site	**Budget**		**Actual**		**Variance favourable/ (adverse)**
Tonnes	3,000		3,400		
	£000		*£000*		*£000*
Revenue		1,275		1,418	143
Materials	801		890		(89)
Labour	153		170		(17)
Power	36		40		(4)
Equipment costs	19		19		
Property costs	27		27		
Administration	35		37		(2)
Marketing and distribution	51		58		(7)
		1,122		1,241	
Operating profit		153		177	24

You are required to:

(a) Explain the type of budget used in the draft budgetary control report, and explain how it links with the firm's long term strategy.

(3 marks)

(b) Explain an alternative to the above budgetary figures and show, using examples, how using your alternative, could help the company to improve organisational performance.

(7 Marks)

(c) The FD has suggested that the firm uses a standard costing system to monitor costs. Explain what this type of system is and how it could benefit CDM.

(5 marks)

Task 3: 15 marks

Evaluating systems and procedures.

You have been asked to carry out a review of CDMs proposed Sales ledger procedures which are outlined below.

In month 1 the invoicing and Sales ledger module of the new IT system goes live. However the Sales Order Processing module which will link to it does not go live until month 3. As a result temporary procedures have been introduced to be used for the interim period when there will be no automatic updates from the sales team or despatch departments to the accounting system.

Ordering and despatch

- Sales staff will be responsible for pricing customers' orders received using an Excel spreadsheet produced for that purpose. A worksheet will be used for each order. Sales staff will be able to view customers' accounts on the IT system and will check their status and credit limits before accepting orders. Once an order is accepted they will print a copy of the worksheet and post it to the customer and email a copy of the worksheet to production and another copy to the Sales Ledger Clerk.
- Production schedules will be planned around customers' orders and once goods are ready for shipping, the order worksheets will be emailed to despatch. Once goods are despatched, the worksheet is updated to show despatch details and emailed to the Sales Ledger Clerk.

Accounting

- The Sales Ledger Clerk is to raise invoices on the basis of worksheets received from despatch. These will be priced automatically by the new software, including VAT where appropriate, and will state the agreed terms of sale and be emailed to the customers.
- Customer queries regarding orders and receipts are directed initially to the sales team. If a credit note is required to solve a problem the Sales Manager will email the Sales Ledger Clerk asking for a credit note to be raised and explaining why this is necessary.
- Customers' statements are run at the month end on the new software and emailed to customers.
- The Assistant Accountant will reconcile the total of the sales ledger balances to the sales ledger control account at the month end.

Using the table on the next page, identify FIVE systemic weaknesses in CDM's proposed internal controls for sales accounting. Explain how each weakness which you have identified could create a problem for the company.

Weakness	Potential problem for the company

Task 4: 15 marks

Analyse decision making and control using management accounting tools.

(1) The Southampton plant is nearing the end of its useful economic life and management are considering whether they should close the site down now or let it continue for a further four years. In the latter case they might be able to raise sufficient finance to invest in the site and continue production there; if this is not possible, they will sell the site.

The production site is near the coast and as a result could be sold for redevelopment as a holiday park. Outline planning permission for this has been given at a cost of £15,000. If the site were to be closed and sold then the firm could expect to receive proceeds of £800,000 (net of legal fees). However staff redundancy payments of £120,000 would need to be paid as would site clean-up costs of £80,000.

It is forecast that the Southampton site will generate cash from malting operations of £275,000 this year after a management recharge of £50,000. This charge is used to allocate a proportion of head office costs to Southampton as the sales team, accounts and HR are all based in Lincolnshire. If Southampton closes, approximately £60,000 of the Southampton business would be transferred to the Lincolnshire site to use up capacity there, although this would put operations there under strain.

Due to the aging of plant at Southampton, maintenance costs are increasing and wastage rates are high. This situation is expected to deteriorate in future so estimates of future cash from operations should be reduced by a further 10% each year.

(a) Calculate the net present value of the proposal to continue to operate the site for the next four years and then selling it. Assume that the site sale proceeds at the end of the four years would be unchanged.

(6 marks)

Year	**0**	**1**	**2**	**3**	**4**
Cash flow					
Discount factor (10%)	1	0.909	0.826	0.751	0.683
Present value					
Net present value					

(b) On financial grounds, recommend whether or not the Southampton site should be sold.

(1 mark)

(c) Identify non-financial factors which should be considered as part of the decision.

(2 marks)

(2) The Southampton plant processes two grades of barley to produce malt. Grade A is used for beer, grade B is used for whisky. Malting processes are identical for the two grades. Costs and revenues are as follows:

	Grade A Barley	**Grade B Barley**
Raw materials cost	£180/tonne	£160/tonne
Other manufacturing costs	£25/tonne	£25/tonne
Malt selling price	£250/tonne	£225/tonne

Machine breakdown at Southampton means that there will not be enough processing time this month to complete all the orders which have been scheduled.

(a) Explain whether production of grade A or grade B malt should be cut back on financial grounds.

(2 marks)

(b) Identify practical steps which should be taken to reduce the impact of the problem.

(2 marks)

(3) CDM is considering producing malt extract at its Lincolnshire plant. Malt extract sells for £300/tonne. It is made from grade C barley, a tonne of grade C barley produces 0.7 tonnes of malt extract. The firm has a target gross profit margin of 22%.

(a) Calculate the target cost of a tonne of malt extract.

(1 mark)

(b) Given that grade C barley costs £140/tonne, calculate the maximum “other manufacturing cost” per tonne of malt extract.

(1 mark)

Task 5: 20 marks

Calculation of ratios and selection of appropriate comments.

(a) Use the financial statements shown below to complete the calculation of financial ratios shown on the next page.

(10 marks)

CD Malt Statement of profit or loss

	Year ended 30.12.20-5	Year ended 30.12.20-6
	£000	*£000*
Revenue	24,158	25,124
Gross profit	5,073	5,527
Operating profit	1,895	2,279
Profit before tax	1,066	985
CD Malt statement of financial position		
Assets		
Non-Current assets	12,841	13,444
Inventories	5,890	6,127
Trade receivables	3,282	3,411
Cash and cash equivalents	158	23
	22,171	23,005
Equities and liabilities		
Equity	10,087	6,772
Non-current liabilities	5,574	10,150
Trade payables	6,398	5,966
Taxation	112	117
	22,171	23,005

Ratios

Show profitability, financial position and liquidity ratios to two decimal places. Working capital ratios should be rounded to the nearest day.

Ratio	Year ended 30.12.20-5	Year ended 30.12.20-6
Profitability		
Gross profit margin %	21.0%	22.0%
Operating profit margin %	7.84%	
Return on capital employed	12.1%	13.47%
Financial position		
Interest cover	2.29 times	
Gearing	35.59%	
Liquidity		
Current ratio	1.43:1	
Quick/acid test ratio	0.53:1	0.56:1
Working capital management		
Inventory holding period	113 days	114 days
Trade receivables collection period	50 days	50 days
Trade payables payment period	123 days	

(b) Select the most appropriate observation about each aspect of the business performance.

(10 Marks)

Profitability

(a) The business has generated more profits in 20-6 than in 20-5	
(b) Growth in sales volumes has caused an increase in the gross profit margin which in its turn has caused an increase in the operating profit margin	
(c) The improvement in the gross profit margin and the operating profit margin could not have been achieved if costs had increased in line with revenue	

Financial position

(a) The company has gone from having low levels of gearing to medium levels of gearing	
(b) The interest cover is healthy, but the level of gearing gives cause for concern	
(c) The company has gone from having medium levels of gearing to high levels of gearing	

Liquidity

(a)	Both liquidity ratios have improved over the year	
(b)	The changes in the ratios are too small to enable meaningful interpretation of the data	
(c)	Both ratios are a cause for concern as the current ratio should not fall below 2:1 and the acid test ratio should not fall below 1:1	

Working capital management

(a)	The working capital cycle has improved by 12 days	
(b)	From the perspective of a supplier the change in the trade payables payment period is a deterioration	
(c)	The change in the trade payables payment period indicates a lack of financial control	

Overall performance

(a)	20-6 has been a good year, sales growth has driven growth in profits and there has only been a moderate increase in gearing	
(b)	Although underlying profitability has improved in 20-6, the level of gearing and resultant interest costs are a significant cause for concern	
(c)	Both underlying profitability and the level of gearing have increased in 20-6; gearing is not an issue as the interest cover remains good	

Task 6: 15 marks

Analyse internal controls and make recommendations.

You have been asked to review CD Malt's purchasing procedures and to make recommendations for improvement.

Grain Purchase planning

Deborah Jones and Paul Arnold, the Sales and Production Directors meet in the run up to harvest to decide on expected sales volumes by category of malt for the coming year. This will feed into plans for the quantity of purchases. Oliver Matthews, the Finance Director, is involved at this point as he will need to make sure that the firm can finance the level of purchases required.

Once plans are agreed, CDM's two buyers will be informed and they will work to achieve the planned levels of purchases. To improve the reliability and quality of supplies, CDM has started to agree long term contracts with farmers who sell the grains. The contracts are fixed price contracts for three years – CDM gets guaranteed supply and the farmers get a guaranteed price, dependant on quality. Initial progress in setting up these contracts was slow, but currently approximately 30% of supply is covered by these agreements. The remainder is bought on the open market and can be imported if required.

Management of grain deliveries

Most farms cannot store the grains for any length of time after harvest so the Buyers schedule deliveries throughout the harvest period. These deliveries will account for approximately 80% of all grain deliveries for the year. CDM use weighbridges to weigh vehicles on arrival with a full load and then vehicles are weighed again on departure to calculate the weight of grain delivered. Copies of weighbridge results are passed to farmers.

A sample of grain from each load is checked to test for quality.

Invoice approval and payment scheduling

Purchase invoices are sent to the buyers for approval, they check the quantities delivered and prices charged. Currently prices need to be checked against physical records of agreements and against the results of the samples inspected on arrival, similarly, the buyers are dependent on printouts of weighbridge records to validate amounts on farmer's invoices.

Once invoices are approved they are passed to the Purchase Ledger Clerk for input onto the accounting system and payments are made according to due dates. Some suppliers have agreed a discounted price for early payment, others have very long terms of trade and are, as a result, paid more.

Other purchases

Purchase orders are required for all other purchases. Purchase orders for other materials need to be approved of by the Production Manager at the relevant site, and are then sent to the buyers who place the orders by email sending a copy to the Purchase Ledger Clerk. GRNs are produced by stores when materials are delivered and copies emailed to the Purchase Ledger Clerk who will match invoices received with approved orders and GRNs before inputting them onto the system. Purchase orders for services such as training or maintenance work need approval by the relevant managers as do the subsequent invoices. Invoices for utilities need approval from the facility managers before they are input onto the system. As with grain purchases, payments are scheduled for invoice due dates.

Payment runs

All payments are made by BACS. On a weekly basis, the Purchase Ledger Clerk generates a report showing invoices due for payment. The report is passed to the Financial Accountant who checks the cash flow position and back-up documentation for about 10% of items listed. Payments may be removed if there is insufficient cash to cover the payment. The approved list is then passed to the Assistant Accountant who generates the BACS payments list which will be approved by the Financial Accountant after checking to make sure that BACS list agrees to the approved payments list. The Purchase Ledger Clerk emails remittance advices to suppliers.

(a) Identify **one** part of the procedures which is a strength. Explain how the business benefits from this.

(4 marks)

(b) Identify **one** weakness in these procedures. Explain how this damages the business and suggest a remedy.

(5 marks)

(c) Identify an opportunity to improve the procedures. Explain how the procedure should be changed and how the business could benefit.

(3 marks)

(d) Identify **one** threat to the effectiveness of these procedures. Explain how this could damage the business.

(3 marks)

Practice synoptic assessment 3

Pre-release material

Company background and history

The Fabled Baker Limited (FBL) is a food manufacturer which runs a chain of bakeries operating in the Midlands. The company owns a factory which produces the majority of the items which are sold in its shops. The company's head office is based with its factory on an industrial estate in Coventry.

The company was started by master baker Peter Taylor and his wife Jean who set up a single bakers' shop in Tamworth in the 1960s. The firm expanded over the years under the management of their children and by the late 1980s had become a limited company owned and managed by the Taylor family with over 80 high street shops. At this point the factory was built and instore bakeries closed. The management of the firm moved to Coventry and consolidated operations as a regional bakery network. Over the next 10 years, the Taylor family became less active in the management of the company.

The firm continued to expand, although at a slower rate, until the start of the recession in 2008. Margins had always been tight due to supermarket competition, but this had been offset by sales volume – which fell dramatically in 2008. Management's response has been to close some shops and to move more clearly into the food-on-the-go market. This has seen the company move back into profitability. The majority of shares in FBL are still owned by the Taylor family, but the current Sales, Production and Finance Directors each have a 10% stake in the company.

In 20-6 FBL had revenue of £42 million, an increase of 3% over 20-5. It runs 73 shops and employs 924 employees, 675 working in the shops, 210 in the factory and distribution and the remainder in Product Development, Administration and Finance.

Mission statement

The Fabled Baker Limited aims to live up to its name, providing high quality and memorable food to all its customers with outstanding levels of customer service.

The firm is, at its core, a family business deeply rooted in the Midlands with a strong work ethic and high degree of loyalty to staff, customers and local communities.

Developments in the market

The trend in declining sales of traditional bakery products such as loaves of bread continues. Alongside this there is significant growth in the market for food-on-the-go. Demand for sandwiches, for savouries such as sausage rolls and pasties, as well as for biscuits and cakes continues to grow. FBL has tried to move its business into the food-on-the-go market by developing new products, such as a breakfast range, and a range of fresh soups. The success of the range of soups has been such that FBL has, for the first time in 20-6, been able to sell these to four supermarket chains for sale in their chilled food sections. The credit sales of soup accounted for 3% of total sales in 20-6. FBL has also invested in coffee machines for its shops and opened a small number of new shops in areas where many people work but where there are few shops.

Several high streets and town centres continue to struggle with the changing demand arising from out of town shopping centres and the rise of online shopping. FBL only closed shops with reluctance in the past and still has several stores which are generating very low profits.

FBL has always paid staff above the minimum wage so the rise of this to £7.20 per hour in April 20-6 has not directly affected it, but staff costs in 20-6 rose by 5% as wage rates were increased to maintain pay differentials. Raw materials prices also rose, partly as a result of the rise in the minimum wage and partly as a result of the uncertainties surrounding the referendum vote for Britain to leave the EU (Brexit).

Strategic planning

The company uses the balanced scorecard to assess its overall performance.

Learning and growth

FBL employs a well-qualified product development team at its factory. They are responsible for constantly reviewing and renewing the firm's product range in line with changing consumer tastes. In 20-6 20% of product lines were "refreshed" and like for like sales responded with growth of 8%. In addition, 56 new products were added to the firm's product portfolio over the year. In week 52 12% of sales were from product lines launched in 20-6. Training requirements of established and of new staff are carefully reviewed and staff regularly attend training sessions at head office – such as in the use of the barista coffee machines.

Business processes

In 20-5 the firm upgraded one production line at its factory and invested in a new soup making production facility. This investment along with the refurbishment of eight shops and the investment in new equipment at all shops combines to increase the capacity of the firm to meet its customers' needs.

Customers

Customer satisfaction is monitored through performance indicators measuring both footfall and average spend per customer in each shop. Both indicators showed positive growth in 20-6. In addition, regular customer satisfaction surveys are carried out, and at the end of 20-6 these show that customers see the firm as offering high quality products and friendly service which is good value for money.

Financial

Revenue grew by 3% in 20-6 and the firm achieved a ROCE of 13%, up from 12% in 20-5. The Taylor family is happy with this improvement, but the three directors are keen to see the company further improve its financial results. They argue that with the level of uncertainty faced by the economy in general FBL needs to make more decisions based on purely financial factors, and in particular to seriously consider closing or re-developing marginally profitable shops.

Staff

FBL's directors responsible for the strategy of the firm overall are:

Managing Director (MD)	Robert Taylor
Production Director (PD)	Brian Stead
Sales Director (SD)	Elaine Anderson
Finance Director (FD)	Alison Davies
Human Resources Director (HRD)	Sanjeev Grover

The Finance Director produces FBL's annual statutory accounts and is responsible for all finance, legal and IT issues. Working for the Finance Director in the accounts team is the Management Accountant, responsible for the standard costing system, the monthly management accounts and annual budgets, the Financial Accountant, responsible for the day-to-day running of the transaction processing systems, and three assistants:

- the Assistant Accountant, responsible for recording shop transactions, bank reconciliations and ad hoc investigations as required
- the Accounts Payable Clerk (Purchase Ledger Clerk), and
- the Payroll and Accounts Receivable(Sales Ledger) Clerk.

FBL's financial statements for 20-6 are shown below.

The Fabled Baker Limited Statement of profit or loss for the year ended 30.12.20-6

Continuing operations	*£000*
Revenue	41,800
Cost of sales	25,916
Gross profit	15,884
Operating expenses	14,667
Operating profit	1,217
Finance costs	41
Profit before tax	1,176
Tax	259
Profit for the period from continuing operations	917

The Fabled Baker Limited Statement of financial position as at 30.12.20-6

	£000
Assets	
Non-Current assets	
Plant property and equipment	11,296
Current assets	
Inventories	1,136
Trade receivables	309
Cash and cash equivalents	61
	12,802
Equities and liabilities	
Ordinary share capital (£1 shares)	2,000
Retained earnings	6,525
Non-current liabilities	
Loans	510
Current liabilities	
Trade payables	3,560
Taxation	207
	12,802

TASKS

Task 1: 20 marks

Multiple choice questions on the topics of roles and responsibilities of the accounting function, preventing and detecting frauds, and ethics.

(a) Link the stakeholders to valid reasons for their interest in the annual statutory accounts of a company. Tick all that apply.

	Lenders	Credit customers	Management
To assess potential for future growth			
To assess security for borrowings			
To assess potential for future dividend payments			

(3 marks)

(b) At FBL, the Payroll and Accounts Receivable Clerk is responsible for issuing sales invoices and statements to credit customers. The Accounts Payable Clerk is responsible for issuing credit notes to customers and the Assistant Accountant records receipts from customers.

When producing the list of aged receivables (debtors) for the monthly management accounts, the Management Accountant notices that one credit note has not been correctly allocated against a receipt.

Which is the most appropriate course of action for the Management Accountant?

(a) Log-in to the accounting system and match the credit note	
(b) Advise the Accounts Payable clerk of the error so that it can be rectified	
(c) Advise the Assistant Accountant of the error so that it can be rectified	
(d) Do nothing – the balance on the account is correct	

(4 marks)

(c) Rolling inventory counts of stores held at FBL's factory are carried out each month. The Assistant Accountant is required to reconcile the inventory counted to the inventory records. A shortfall of material FG442 held in stores has been identified. State whether the following problems could have caused the shortage.

Problem	Could have caused shortage	Would not cause shortage
(a) Receipt of goods incorrectly keyed in as 100 units instead of 1,000 units		
(b) Theft of stores		
(c) Issue of stores to production incorrectly keyed in as 100 units instead of 1,000 units		
(d) A container of goods on the production line was counted twice		
(e) Stock records not updated for disposal of out-of-date inventory		

(5 marks)

(d) Which of the controls below are aimed at the prevention of errors?

(a)	Bank reconciliation	
(b)	Accounting system will not accept transactions with a future date	
(c)	Analysis of costs by department and investigation of variances in the monthly management accounts	
(d)	Audit trails show which user posted each transaction	
(e)	Credit notes need to be raised by a clerk and checked by the Financial Accountant before they are passed for posting	

(3 marks)

(e) At year-end the balance of cash at bank has dipped significantly lower than planned. Jamie Taylor, who currently works in production, suggests that the cash book should be left open for a couple of days to capture cash receipts from shops and boost the bank balance.

What **one** ethical principle is most threatened by this suggestion?

(Select from: Professional Behaviour, professional competence and due care, confidentiality, integrity and objectivity.)

(3 marks)

(f) Trudi Taylor has been investigating the amounts of unsold food in shops at the end of each day and whether or not it can be given to charities such as soup kitchens. She asks for support from the Finance Director and says that he has an ethical duty as an accountant to support sustainability.

This statement is | true/false |.

(2 marks)

Task 2: 15 marks

Evaluating budgetary reporting.

FBL goes through an annual budgeting process whereby the Management Accountant discusses shop results with the Sales and Production Directors. Trends in shop sales and in sales of individual products are analysed along with refurbishment plans and forecasts for inflation. The data is pulled together by the Management Accountant who then produces draft budgets for each shop which are then discussed and approved by the board before being issued to shop managers.

(a) Explain what is meant by 'Top-down budgeting' and give an example of one advantage of the way this method is applied at FBL.

(3 marks)

(b) Explain what is meant by 'Participative budgeting' and suggest one benefit that might arise if FBL were to adopt it.

(3 marks)

FBL use a budgetary control report as part of their monthly management accounts which is flexed to actual results. The summary budget is backed up by detailed analysis of results both on a shop by shop basis and by product line.

A new shop manager complains that she does not understand why her budgeted figures have been changed in the budgetary control report. She says that she feels that there is no point in having a budget at all if the figures are changed every month.

(c) Explain the purpose of a flexed budget and how it helps to control costs in an organisation.

(3 marks)

The Management Accountant is off sick and some detailed figures need to be calculated. In particular the materials variances for the 'Winter Warmer Tomato Soup' are to be analysed.

(d) Calculate the raw materials price and usage variances for the 'Winter Warmer tomato soup'.

The standard costs of a portion of soup include 0.3 kg of raw materials with a standard cost of £2 per kg. During period 12, the company produced and sold 5,460 portions of soup. 1,660 kgs of raw materials were used with a cost of £3,569.

Raw Material price variance £ [ ] favourable/(adverse)

Raw material usage variance £ [ ] favourable/(adverse)

(4 marks)

(e) Explain what information this detailed analysis gives you that is not shown in the flexed budget and how this helps to control costs in the firm.

(2 marks)

Task 3: 15 marks

Evaluating systems and procedures.

You have been asked to review the controls in the credit saies system at FBL and have established the following.

Background

FBL's sales team deal with shop products and promotions as opposed to credit sales. Credit sales started when FBL was contacted by a supermarket wanting to know if they would be interested in supplying them with their fresh soups. The Buyer making the call was a keen soup buying customer at FBL and knew that their employer was looking to increase both its range of fresh chilled foods and its product portfolio from the local region. The Product Development Manager was delighted by the opportunities in this new market and has been contacting other supermarkets and negotiating sales with them ever since. There are currently four credit customers, all of whom have deliveries on a daily basis to their regional distribution centres.

Ordering and delivery

Purchase orders from the supermarkets are emailed to the Product Development Manager who uses the accounting system's sales order processing module to record them and communicate the orders to the Production Manager. Once production is complete, despatch notes are produced from the accounting software and a hard copy is given to the delivery driver who will get the customer's signature for receipt of the goods. The signed copies are returned to the Payroll and Accounts Receivable Clerk who then uses the accounting software to raise sales invoices which are posted to customers.

Recording receipts and account management

The supermarkets pay by BACS on 90 day terms. The accounting software used by FBL has a sales ledger module which is integrated with the nominal ledger and with the sales order processing module. Invoices raised automatically update customers' accounts. The Assistant Accountant downloads a bank statement on a daily basis and updates ledgers for receipts. Should there be disputes with customers about the quality or quantity of deliveries, these are investigated by the Accounts Payable Clerk who will produce credit notes as required. Credit notes need authorisation by the Financial Accountant, once authorisation has been obtained they are posted to the customers' accounts. Statements are posted to customers on a monthly basis by the Payroll and Accounts Receivable Clerk. An aged receivables (debtors) report is included in the monthly management accounts.

Using the table on the next page, identify FIVE systemic weaknesses in FBL's internal controls for credit sales accounting. Explain how each weakness which you have identified could create a problem for the company.

Weakness	Potential problem for the company

Task 4: 15 marks

Analyse decision making and control using management accounting tools.

FBL uses traditional overhead absorption methods to allocate and apportion overheads to units produced. The Management Accountant is investigating the option of introducing activity based costing and you are asked to perform some preliminary calculations for this.

Included in overheads which are absorbed into production on the basis of machine hours is £180,000 per annum spent on product development. This includes the cost of redesigning products, of test bakes, approval and set-up for mass production.

In 20-6 the recipes for a total of 90 products were designed or re-designed.

(a) Calculate the activity based costing cost driver recovery rate for product development.

£ [ ] per recipe.

(2 marks)

The 90 products designed includes sausage rolls and all of the soups produced during the year. Once the new recipe for sausage rolls was agreed, the recipe was used all year (300 working days), but each soup recipe was only used for four weeks (24 working days).

Each working day 7,000 sausage rolls were produced and 1,000 litres of soup were produced.

(b) Using an activity based costing approach, calculate the cost of product development in pence to two decimal places per litre of soup.

[ ] pence per litre of soup.

(3 marks)

(c) Using an activity based costing approach, calculate the cost of product development in pence to two decimal places per sausage roll.

[ ] pence per sausage roll.

(3 marks)

(d) Explain how the introduction of activity based costing might improve decision making at FBL.

(3 marks)

(e) Give **one** example of a type of overhead cost for which activity based costing cannot give more accurate information than absorption costing, and explain why this is the case.

(2 marks)

(f) Another idea for improving management information at FBL which is being investigated is product life cycle costing. Explain what is meant by this concept and the potential benefits which it can bring.

(2 marks)

Task 5: 20 marks

Calculation of ratios and selection of appropriate comments.

(a) Use the financial statements shown to complete the calculation of financial ratios shown below.

(10 marks)

Statement of profit or loss	**Year ended 31.12.20-6**	**6 months ended 31.12.20-6**
	£000	*£000*
	High Street shop	**New out of town shop**
	£000	£000
Revenue	389	230
Gross profit	136	90
Operating profit	4	12
Profit before tax	3	10
Statement of financial position	**31.12.20-6**	**31.12.20-6**
Assets	*£000*	*£000*
Non-Current assets	43	201
Inventories	8	6
Cash and cash equivalents	1	1
	52	208
Financed by		
Non-current inter-company loan	52	208

Ratios

Show profitability ratios to two decimal places. Working capital ratios should be rounded to the nearest day.

Ratio	**Company overall**	**High Street Shop**	**New out of town shop**
Profitability			
Gross profit margin %	38%	34.96%	39.13%
Operating profit margin %	2.91%	1.03%	
Asset turnover	4.63 times		2.21 times
Return on capital employed	13.47%		
Inventory holding period	16 days		8 days

(b) Complete the commentary on FBL's shop results below, deleting as appropriate.

(10 Marks)

1. Profit margins at **the high street shop/the new shop/both shops** give cause for concern.

2. Operating profit margins indicate that overheads make up a **similar/different** proportion of revenue at the two shops.

3. Relative to the assets invested, **the high street shop/the new shop/both shops** are operating at levels of profitability lower than the company average.

4. A new shop will go through its own product life cycle and at the growth stage would be expected to have **low/medium/high** levels of profitability.

5. The return on capital employed of the long established high street shop may be **inflated/depressed** if non-current assets have not been revalued.

6. The asset turnover of the new out of town shop may be **inflated/depressed** because of the value of recently purchased land and buildings.

7. The benchmark return on capital employed for similar businesses is 20%. If FBL want to move closer to this level of return they need to consider closing stores such as **the high street shop/the new shop/both shops**.

8. Inventory holding periods at both stores are better than the company average which is probably due to **efficiencies at the shops/the fact that the majority of inventories are kept at the factory**.

9. Management are **likely/not likely** to be concerned about the performance of the high street shop.

10. Management are **likely/not likely** to be concerned about the performance of the new out of town shop.

Task 6: 15 marks

Analyse internal controls and make recommendations.

Staff costs make up over 40% of FBL's costs and the biggest component of these costs relate to hourly paid shop workers – ie, all shop staff other than the shop managers who are salaried.

You have been asked to carry out a review of FBL's wages procedures for hourly paid shop staff and to make recommendations for improvement. The current systems are detailed below.

Recruitment and shift planning

Shop managers are responsible for the level of staffing in their shops. If they feel they need more staff, positions will be advertised and shop managers are responsible for interviewing and selecting new employees, for passing relevant documentation to HR and for arranging for new employees to attend induction training at head office. HR record details of new starters on the payroll system. HR are also responsible for removing all leavers from this system once these have been notified by shop managers.

Shop managers all use a standard spreadsheet to plan shifts. Rotas are displayed in shops two weeks in advance and the shift rota is emailed to the Payroll Clerk at the same time.

Staff book holidays with their shop manager, this is recorded on an HR spreadsheet, updates of which are sent to HR on a weekly basis. HR monitor staff holidays and any sick leave, etc.

Time recording

Employees use smart cards to clock in and out of shops. Clocking data is downloaded from the clocking terminal onto a USB stick by the shop managers at the end of each day and emailed to the Payroll Clerk for analysis and processing. The Payroll Clerk uploads the data and runs exception reports to check that the data is within expected parameters. High or low numbers of hours are checked back to the shift rotas to check their validity.

Payroll

FBL use a standard accounting software package for payroll which is RTI compliant (UK HMRC Real Time Information). This comes with automatic updates and support provided via telephone helpdesk. The Payroll Clerk exports the details of shop staff hours worked into the payroll package on a daily basis, and four working days before the end of the month, runs a monthly payroll. Check prints are produced showing employee costs for each shop as well as details for all starters and leavers. These prints are passed to the Financial Accountant who spends two to three hours reviewing them with the Payroll Clerk.

After the payroll has been agreed, the Payroll Clerk produces a BACS transfer authority which is signed by two of the authorising signatories – these are the Financial Accountant and the Directors. Staff are paid by BACS on the last working day of the month.

(a) Identify **one** part of the procedures which is a strength. Explain how the business benefits from this.

(4 marks)

(b) Identify **one** weakness in these procedures. Explain how this damages the business and suggest a remedy.

(5 marks)

(c) Identify an opportunity to improve the procedures. Explain how the procedure should be changed and how the business could benefit.

(3 marks)

(d) Identify **one** threat to the effectiveness of these procedures. Explain how this could damage the business.

(3 marks)

Practice synoptic assessment 4

Pre-release material

Company background and history

EG Products Ltd (EGP) is a manufacturer of refuse collection equipment. The main source of revenue is the sale of refuse collection vehicles along with steel recycling banks, of the type commonly used for collection of paper and cardboard. A second stream of revenue comes from the maintenance and repair of the vehicles.

EGP has its head office on an industrial estate near Newcastle upon Tyne. The site includes both production facilities and offices from which the business is managed. The company was founded in the 1980s initially servicing a single local government sub-contractor. At that point, the firm was owner-managed, however external equity investment was required to finance the firm's expansion and to ensure that production facilities were first class. Each of the five directors has a 10% stake in the equity of the firm, the balance of shares are held by private equity providers.

In 20-6, the company generated revenue of £18 million, it employs 135 FTE employees, 115 of whom work in production either in the factory or as field engineers, the balance being office staff working in sales and administration.

Mission statement

EGP aims to: use the best raw materials for each item produced, to have production processes which will ensure that all output is of the highest standard and to complete maintenance and services to the highest standards.

EGP is committed to giving customers great value for money, developing our employees, working in fair partnership with our suppliers and promoting sustainability.

Developments in the market

There are several opposing forces affecting the size of the market within which EGP operates. Firstly, customers are either local authorities or private businesses to whom councils have sub-contracted work. Central government cuts since 2010 have significantly reduced the size of budgets for waste management in these organisations. One result of this is that vehicles are often used more intensively - for instance by double shifting them. This could involve them being run as an early shift collecting general waste and then as a late shift collecting recycling on the same day. Another result is that the working lives of both vehicles and recycling banks are extended. Whilst this is not good news for the sales of new products, EGP does benefit from increased repair and maintenance work in this instance.

A second feature of the market which is causing change is the drive towards sustainability. The EU target, towards which all UK local authorities are working, is to increase the recycling rate from approximately 41% of rubbish collected in 2010 to 50% by 2020. In Scotland the goal is to recycle 60% of household waste by 2020 and 70% of all waste by 2025. The introduction of new services to meet these goals drives capital expenditure on recycling equipment.

In addition to the above, the market will be affected by the referendum vote for Britain to leave the EU (Brexit). It is currently unclear for how long EU subsidy schemes offering grants in support of council recycling projects will continue to operate.

Strategic planning

The company uses the balanced scorecard to assess its overall performance.

Learning and growth

EGP constantly invests in product development. Recent innovations include the development of new vehicles which require fewer operators (enabling savings in staff costs), the ability to install hybrid engines in refuse vehicles, and options to install in-cab technology and CCTV. Managers formally review staff performance and individual training needs twice a year to ensure that the skills of the workforce keep up with the rate of product development and to enable the company to respond flexibly to a changing market place.

Business processes

EGP uses computer aided design software to ensure that all product designs are of the highest standard. Investment in production equipment – such as the laser cutting equipment and the welding robots in use - helps to ensure that the firm has the capacity to produce items of the highest quality, and rigorous inspection and testing procedures ensure that production has achieved that level of quality. The firm monitors quality problems, including production delays, customer complaints and repairs under warranty. EGP is an affiliate member of CIWM (Chartered Institute of Waste Management) and of VBRA (Vehicle Builders and Repairers Association).

Customers

EGP has an 'After–Sales Department' who manage relationships with customers both when new products are under warranty and where EGP has a maintenance or service contract with the customer. Customer satisfaction surveys are completed regularly both on receipt of a new vehicle, after operative training for the vehicle and once the vehicle is in use. Follow up calls are made by the After-sales team to check on customer satisfaction after services or maintenance work has been completed. Levels of customer satisfaction are high in almost all areas, although EGP is not always as competitive on price as it would like to be, but it does not have the economies of scale of some of its rivals.

Financial

Sales units in 20-6 grew by 4% compared with 20-5, however price competition meant that revenue only grew by 2%.

Staff

FBL's directors responsible for the strategy of the firm overall are:

Managing Director (MD)	Andrea Heppell
Production Director (PD)	Glenn MacArthur
Sales Director (SD)	Gloria Clarke
Finance Director (FD)	Martin Boyd
Human Resources Director (HRD)	Narissa Sealy

The Finance Director has overall responsibility for all Finance, Legal and IT issues and for producing the annual statutory accounts. His team works well having all worked at the firm for at least two years and having a good understanding of the business and their own roles. Staff are as follows:

- Financial Accountant, responsible for the work of the accounts clerks, for production of the monthly management accounts and compilation of budgets.
- Assistant Accountant, completing the roles of Cashier and of Accounts Receivable Clerk (Sales Ledger Clerk)
- Accounts Payable Clerk (Purchase Ledger Clerk)
- Payroll and General Ledger Clerk

Date

It is early January 20-7.

EGP's financial statements for 2016 are shown below.

EG Products Ltd Statement of profit or loss for the year ended 30.12.20-6

Continuing operations	*£000*
Revenue	18,237
Cost of sales	15,137
Gross profit	3,100
Operating expenses	2,735
Operating profit	365
Finance costs	45
Profit before tax	320
Tax	64
Profit for the period from continuing operations	256

EG Products Ltd Statement of financial position as at 30.12.20-6

	£000
Assets	
Non-Current assets	
Plant property and equipment	654
Current assets	
Inventories	2,613
Trade receivables	2,148
Cash and cash equivalents	707
	6,122
Equities and liabilities	
Ordinary share capital (£1 shares)	2,000
Retained earnings	1,956
Non-current liabilities	
Loans	500
Current liabilities	
Trade payables	1,617
Taxation	49
	6,122

TASKS

Task 1: 20 marks

Multiple choice questions on the topics of roles and responsibilities of the accounting function, preventing and detecting frauds, and ethics.

(a) The table below shows a range of purchase related queries. Which should be directed to the Accounts Department and which should be dealt with by the Purchasing team?

Department	Accounts department	Purchasing team
(a) Preferred supplier for a particular purchased component		
(b) Financial stability of new supplier		
(c) Agreed price lists **(d)** Due date for payment of invoice		

(4 marks)

(b) The Purchasing Manager asks Martin Boyd, the Finance Director for the assistance of the Accounts Payable Clerk in evaluating the costs of power supplies for the factory. There are six different options to be investigated and the Purchasing Manager would like the Accounts Payable Clerk to carry out the analysis.

Which is the most appropriate response to this request? (Tick **one** option.)

(a) The Purchasing Manager is in charge of purchasing decisions so the investigation should be carried out by the Purchasing team	
(b) It is appropriate for the Accounts Payable Clerk to help if s/he has time available as the work should contribute to the solvency and cost effectiveness of the firm – these are key factors which the Accounts Department tries to control	
(c) The Accounts Payable Clerk should do the work and Martin Boyd should make the decision about the most appropriate package as he is responsible for the finances of the organisation	

(2 marks)

(c) In addition to running the monthly payroll, the Payroll and General Ledger Clerk is responsible for updating the Non-current Asset register and recording depreciation as well as carrying out weekly bank reconciliations.

Identify which of the following statements are true/false.

Statements	True	False
(a) There is an increased risk that non-current assets will be purchased for employee use		
(b) The review of audit trails showing details of the originator of each transaction will detect any frauds which may have been carried out		
(c) The Financial Accountant should check the bank reconciliations and ensure that payroll amounts paid agree to authorised payroll prints		

(3 marks)

(d) The Payroll and General Ledger Clerk asks whether the following errors and omissions would be detected by carrying out a bank reconciliation:

Problem	Would be detected	Would not be detected
(a) Bank interest charged has been recorded in the cash book as bank interested received		
(b) The bank has made a payment in error		
(c) A customer has deducted a prompt payment discount to which they were not entitled		

(3 marks)

(e) Two IT system controls are shown in the table below together with three threats to the integrity of data held on the IT system. You are to tick the control column if that control will help to protect the accounting data from the threat given.

Control / Threat	Automatic back-ups of data are made every time a user posts a transaction	User profiles restrict staff access to the accounting system so that only authorised tasks can be performed
(a) Data is lost due to a power cut		
(b) Production staff try to change accounting data		
(c) Infection of computer system by a computer virus		

(2 marks)

(f) A student from a local college was completing work experience with the Purchasing team. She took a phone call during which the caller claimed to be from a key supplier who, said the caller, had suffered a computer failure and had lost all their data. The caller asked for key details of the suppliers' contract with EGP, including quantities, prices and discounts. The student gave out the details as requested. The call turns out to have been bogus.

(1) Which of the fundamental accounting principles has been most clearly breached by what has occurred? (Select from: Professional Behaviour, professional competence and due care, confidentiality, integrity and objectivity.)

(2) Given that the student was on work experience, can the company be held liable for what has occurred? (Yes/ No)

(3) Has the Data Protection Act been breached? (Yes/ No)

(6 marks)

Task 2: 15 marks

Evaluating budgetary reporting

In early December 20-6 the budget for 20-7 is prepared ready for board meetings and communication to department managers. This involves the Financial Accountant in particular, working overtime at an already busy time of year.

(a) Explain the purposes that will be served by having approved budgets in place for the start of 20-7.

(6 marks)

The draft budget for raw materials costs for 20-7 is shown below.

Materials purchasing budget for 20-7

Products	**20-6 Units**	**20-6 Actual materials and components cost** *£000*	**20-7 Sales Units**	**20-7 Budget materials and componenets cost** *£000*
Vehicles	220	7,885	229	8,290
Recycling banks	188	374	196	394
Maintenance and services	1,589 jobs	633	1,653	665
	Total	**8,892**	**Total**	**9,349**

The purchasing budget shown above has been prepared on the assumption that sales volumes will increase by 4% in 20-7 as they did in 20-6. In addition it has been assumed that raw materials and components prices will rise by 1%.

In the light of changing economic conditions post Brexit, it is now expected that vehicle and recycling bank sales will only increase by 1% in volume. However, sales of maintenance and services are expected to grow by 5%. It is also predicted that a fall in the value of sterling will lead to an average price rise for raw materials of 5%.

(b) Complete the table below to calculate a revised materials purchasing budget for 20-7. Round your answers to the nearest whole number.

(6 marks)

Products	**20-7 Sales Units**	**20-7 Budget materials and components cost** *£000*
Vehicles		
Recycling banks		
Maintenance and services		
	Total	

(c) For sales of recycling banks suggest **two** possible performance indicators which could be used to monitor raw materials costs.

(3 marks)

Task 3: 15 marks

Evaluating systems and procedures

You have been asked to review the purchasing and payment procedures at EFP. Purchasing and payment procedures have gone unchanged for well over five years – they were last updated when the current accounting system was installed. Although the systems are not documented staff know and understand them well and problems or queries are usually sorted quickly.

Purchase ordering raw materials and components

Purchase requisitions are issued by the Stores Manager, for items constantly in use by the Production Manager for items required for particular jobs, and by the After-Sales Manager for items required for servicing or maintenance jobs.

The accounting system includes a purchase ordering module which is used by purchasing clerks to check requisitions received against the computerised inventory records and against the quotes for future work on the job costing system. The purchasing clerks then create pre-numbered purchase orders using 'Approved Suppliers' and quoting the most recent agreed price for the component or material required. Purchase orders are printed, checked and authorised by the Purchasing Manager and then posted out to suppliers. A signed copy is sent to accounts for matching to invoices.

Receipts

Deliveries of raw materials and components are dealt with by stores who check the quality of items received. Deliveries are matched to purchase orders and stores staff update the inventory module of the accounting system for the goods received and create GRNs (Goods Received Notes).

Invoice approval and supplier account maintenance

The Accounts Payable Clerk is responsible for all updates to the purchase ledger, both setting up suppliers and recording purchase invoices received. Invoices received are matched to purchase orders and to GRNs. Each invoice is stamped with a table requiring details of the purchase order, the GRN number and the accounts code to which it is to be posted. These references must be entered and all details matched for each reference before the accounting system will allow the posting of the invoice. If invoices are sent by email, they are printed so that they can be stamped and checked. There is always a folder of invoices awaiting processing as some or all details have not been matched to purchase orders and GRNs, this can lead to delays in paying invoices and occasionally to EGP's accounts with suppliers being put on stop.

The Accounts Payable Clerk is responsible for investigating any discrepancies between purchase orders, deliveries and invoices, for arranging credit notes as appropriate and for reconciling supplier statements received. Invoices are filed by month and within that by supplier, and are archived after a couple of months.

Fuel and expenses

Field engineers commonly need to travel to customer depots to carry out repairs or maintenance work on site. The field engineers are given company credit cards to enable them to pay for fuel for their vehicles, for one-off purchases of parts and for accommodation should it be required. Engineers are required to keep receipts for all payments and these are passed to the Accounts Payable Clerk. Credit card statements are passed to the Accounts Payable Clerk who checks that all payments match up with valid receipts before coding the costs to the relevant jobs and filing the statements with the other purchase invoices.

Payments

An aged creditors report is run by the Accounts Payable Clerk twice a month to identify invoices due for payment. The Financial Accountant checks the list and approves items to be paid. The list is passed to the Assistant Accountant who generates a BACS payment run. This is checked back to the approved list by the Financial Accountant before signing it. One of the Directors will also check and sign the list as two signatures are required. Remittance advices are generated by the Assistant Accountant and posted to suppliers.

Urgent payments can be made by cheque if required, but this is discouraged as it is a time consuming, expensive and slow method of payment. Blank cheques are stored in the Assistant Accountant's desk.

Identify FIVE systemic weaknesses in EGP's internal controls for purchasing and payments. Explain how each weakness which you have identified could create a problem for the company.

Weakness	Potential problem for the company

Task 4: 15 marks

Analyse decision making and control using management accounting tools

Part 1

The Financial Accountant is considering upgrading the accounting system. The option being considered is the installation of software which would allow the accounting system to use scanned images of all purchase invoices as opposed to hard copies as at present.

Invoices would be scanned on receipt and stored as pdfs. Any invoices sent as pdfs by email would be uploaded directly. Any hard copy invoices received would be shredded. The software being investigated is acceptable to HMRC for record keeping and archiving purposes. Initially the status of uploaded invoices would be 'unmatched', but the status would change as the invoice was matched to the purchase order and the goods received record. Reports could be run to show the invoices and their value at each stage of the process.

The IT system upgrade, including software purchase would cost £2,400. Training of the Accounts Payable Clerk to use the system would be carried out by the software company's installer at this stage and would take three hours. It is assumed that the Accounts Payable Clerk could train other staff to use the system as required. The Accounts Payable clerk is paid £8 per hour. Employer's NI and other employer costs can be assumed to amount to 14% of wages.

You have been asked to start on the work which will lead to a cost-benefit analysis of the proposed upgrade.

(a) Quantify an incremental financial cost of the implementation of the purchase invoice scanning system.

(1 mark)

Cost	£

(b) Explain what is meant by an opportunity cost.

(1 mark)

(c) Explain what the opportunity cost of training the Accounts Payable Clerk will be and calculate the value of this to EGP.

(2 marks)

(d) Identify a financial benefit of the implementation of the purchase invoice scanning system.
Note: You will not be able to cost this from the above information. (2 marks)

(e) Explain a non-financial cost of the implementation of the purchase invoice scanning system.

(2 marks)

(f) Explain a non-financial benefit of the implementation of the purchase invoice scanning system and its effects on the company.

(2 marks)

Part 2

The servicing and maintenance side of EGPs business has been steadily growing since the economic downturn in 2008. The number of field engineers has grown much more slowly than sales, as EGP have tried to use employees to full capacity.

At the start of week 7, urgent orders for maintenance work are received from local authorities as follows.

	Council 5	Council 8	Council 17
Sales price of work	£2,300	£800	£1,650
Materials, components and expenses	£1,104	£352	£924
Engineers hours required	40	14	24

Field engineers are paid £18 per hour. There are a total of 48 hours available to work on these contracts in the coming week.

Complete the table below to show the work allocation which will maximise the contribution earned from field engineers in week 7. You can assume that work started in week 7 can be completed in week 8.

(5 marks)

	Council 5	Council 8	Council 17
Contribution from order (£s)			
Contribution per hour (£s)			
Hours allocated to job			

Task 5: 20 marks

Calculation of ratios and selection of appropriate comments

One of EGP's suppliers, Casper Components Ltd, is in financial difficulties and needs an injection of capital. Casper Components contacts EGP to suggest that the company may like to invest in them. Advantages to EGP would include being assured of preferential treatment as a customer of Casper Components as well as being able to have a say in the direction of travel of the company – for instance with regards to quality or product development. Casper is looking for an investment of £1 million.

(a) Use the financial statements shown below to complete the calculation of financial ratios shown on the next page.

(10 marks)

Casper Components Ltd statement of profit or loss

	Year ended 30.6.20-5	Year ended 30.6.20-6
	£000	*£000*
Revenue	18,861	20,748
Gross profit	6,601	7,054
Operating profit	1,225	990
Profit before tax	1,019	685
Statement of financial position		
Assets		
Non-Current assets	3,918	4,214
Inventories	2,015	2,551
Trade receivables	2,429	2,785
Cash and cash equivalents	34	
	8,396	9,550
Equities and liabilities		
Equity	4,359	4,451
Non-current liabilities	2,575	3,350
Cash and cash equivalents		32
Trade payables	1,310	1,613
Taxation	152	104
	8,396	9,550

Ratios

Show profitability, financial position and liquidity ratios to two decimal places. Working capital ratios should be rounded to the nearest day.

Ratio	Year ended 30.6.20-5	Year ended 30.6.20-6
Profitability		
Gross profit margin %	35%	34%
Operating profit margin %	6.49%	4.77%
Return on capital employed %	17.67%	
Financial position		
Interest cover	5.95	3.25
Gearing (debt/equity)	59.07%	
Liquidity		
Current ratio	3.06:1	3.05:1
Quick/acid test ratio	1.68:1	
Working capital management		
Inventory holding period	60 days	68 days
Trade receivables collection period	47 days	
Trade payables payment period	30 days	43 days
Working capital cycle	68 days	

(b) Select the **one** correct observation about each aspect of Casper Component Ltd's performance below.

(10 Marks)

Profitability

(a) Casper Components Ltd earns higher operating profit margins on its sales than EGP does	
(b) The fall in the operating profit margin is caused both by the reduction in the gross profit margin and by the increase in operating expenses as a proportion of revenue	
(c) Casper Components Ltd explain that they had to cut selling prices in 20-6 to boost sales. This factor accounts for the reduction in the firm's return on capital employed	

Financial position

(a)	The current level of interest cover is a cause for concern	
(b)	The current level of gearing indicates that the majority of the firm's finance is provided by loan finance	
(c)	Casper Components Ltd has medium levels of gearing	

Liquidity

(a)	Casper Components Ltd current ratios could indicate that it is holding too many current assets	
(b)	Both the current ratios and acid test ratios are satisfactory because current ratios should always be more than 2:1 and the acid test ratios should always be more than 1:1	
(c)	Although the acid test ratio has declined this is more than offset by the stability of the current ratio	

Working capital management

(a)	The changes to all the working capital ratios could result from overtrading	
(b)	The increased trade receivables collection period could result from changes to credit terms or an increased focus on debt collection	
(c)	The increase in the trade payables payment period can only be interpreted as a cause for concern	

Summary

(a)	EGP should not invest in Casper Components Ltd as the company is less profitable than EGP and is too risky	
(b)	EGP should consider investing in Casper Components Ltd as it generates returns higher than EGP does	
(c)	EGP will be unable to access the funds required to invest in Casper Components Ltd so cannot make this investment	

Task 6: 15 marks

Analyse internal controls and make recommendations

You have been asked to carry out a review of EGP's sales procedures and to make recommendations for improvements.

Current procedures are outlined below.

Tendering for council contracts

All bids for council work are managed by Gloria Clarke, the Sales Director, who, at the age of 64 has encyclopaedic knowledge of local government procurement procedures and over ten years' experience in her current role. Her technical team who will work on bids for her include EGP's Product Development Manager with a team of two engineers – all of whom are adept users of the CAD software – the Production Manager, whose input is required to ensure that bids are submitted in line with production capabilities and the Purchasing Manager.

Website

The company's website is used to advertise its refuse collection vehicles and recycling banks more generally and includes an overview of the company and its products together with testimonials and links to 'Get a quote' as well as the sales team's contact details. Most of EGP's private work is generated by the website.

Contracts with customers

Formal sales contracts are signed with all local authorities and private companies before work is started on any refuse collection vehicles. If an order is received from a new customer the Assistant Accountant carries out a credit check on this company using an online credit referencing agency. One bank and two supplier references are reviewed before credit is granted; the Assistant Accountant then sends out standard terms of trade for signing. The terms of trade include clear retention of title clauses.

Invoicing

Despatch notes are issued for all completed products and customer signatures collected and returned to the Accounts Department for filing as proof of delivery. Invoices are generated automatically when products are despatched and are posted to customers.

Where servicing and maintenance work is carried out (except for warranty work) a job card is created to record the costs of the work. Field Engineers update manual job cards with their hours and parts used whilst on the road, and then pass the cards to a clerk for input on their return to the office. This can be up to a week after the completion of the job. The Assistant Accountant downloads copies of completed jobs on a daily basis and generates the relevant invoices which are posted to customers.

(a) Identify **one** part of the procedures which is a strength. Explain how the business benefits from this.

(4 marks)

(b) Identify **one** weakness in these procedures. Explain how this damages the business and suggest a remedy.

(5 marks)

(c) Identify an opportunity to improve the procedures. Explain how the procedure should be changed and how the business could benefit.

(3 marks)

(d) Identify **one** threat to the effectiveness of these procedures. Explain how this could damage the business.

(3 marks)

Answers to practice synoptic assessment 1

Task 1

(a) **(a)**, **(c)** and **(d)** are valid; **(b)** and **(e)** are not valid

(b) (b) Prepare the sales invoice as normal, but also keep a copy of the job sheet and send the original back to the relevant Branch Manager for investigation

(c) **(a)**, **(b)** and **(e)** would be detected; **(c)** and **(d)** would not be detected

(d) (e) All of the above

(e) **(1)** Professional behaviour, Integrity

(2) (b) The National Crime Agency

Task 2

(a) Assumptions – Sales will double and all costs will rise in proportion – are there sound reasons for assuming that sales will double? It seems like guesswork. The split of fixed costs and variable costs may not be the same for a small branch as for a large branch, but this has not been considered. Barnstaple cost profile may not be similar to Exeter's – Exeter is a city, Barnstaple is not, Exeter is not a good branch to use as a model. The assumption that staff costs will be 38% of revenue may also not be correct.

(b) This is an example of a top-down budget set as target for junior management. Whilst the Barnstaple manager is new and inexperienced and may work hard to achieve targets set by more experienced senior managers, the lack of detailed planning that has gone into the targets will make them unrealistic as targets. The Barnstaple manager will not be motivated by the budget – targets must be challenging and achievable to be effective as motivators.

(c) Standard costing is useful in an environment where there is routine production of identical items – unit costs can be planned in a lot of detail and deviations from them monitored. However ABL is a service company and production is not standard. A standard costing system would be expensive to set-up and to update – and is unlikely to be justifiable in this company.

(d) Rolling budgets are ones which are continuously updated. They are planned in a lot of detail for the short term, but have only general details filled in for the longer term. So in this case a detailed budget could be produced for January 20-6 and February 20-6 and an outline budget for the subsequent months of 20-6. Towards the end of January a detailed budget for March 20-6 could be produced and an outline budget for January 20-7. At the end of February 20-6 a detailed budget for April 20-6 would be added along with an outline budget for February 20-7. Rolling budgets would help to give the Barnstaple branch manager meaningful targets and also help senior management to understand the trajectory of the new branch, so it would be useful to introduce them.

(e) Any two from:

- cost variances against quote for installations
- % installations completed on time
- chargeable hours/engineer/month
- call outs/engineer/day
- vans – mpg
- % first time fix for each engineer
- average miles per call-out
- gross profit margin % per job

Task 3

Weakness	Potential problem for the company
Engineers' timesheets filed at branch – no one at head office can check if authorised or if amounts input agree to amounts authorised	Fraud – collusion between engineers and branch clerk
Payroll clerk has full user rights	Can change rates of pay, rates of pension contributions, add employees – fraud risk
Branch managers can add temporary staff	Fraud risk – fictitious employees, risk of breaching employment regulations if branch manager does not carry out relevant checks
Financial Accountant has partial training on payroll software	What if Payroll Clerk is ill – is this enough? Staff could have financial problems if they are paid late
Financial Accountant checks are limited – no check of starters and leavers, no check of deductions, or pension contributions	Payroll Clerk errors or fraud could go undetected
No overall reconciliation from Userve to payroll system for branch engineers' wages	Payroll hours could be input incorrectly onto payroll system and engineers' wages overpaid
The Financial Accountant authorises the BACS payment	Potential fraud by Financial Accountant

Task 4

Part 1

(a) £15,400/£10 = 1,540 hours to break-even

1,540/140 = 11 engineers to break-even

(b) 2/11 x 100 = 18.18%

(c) In decision-making the only costs that should be considered are those that change as a result of the decision. The costs of running the Barnstaple office are relevant to decisions about opening it. Head office costs will be incurred whatever the decision is about opening the site and are not relevant to this decision. Barnstaple is still viable for January.

Part 2

(a)

Time	**0**	**1**	**2**	**3**	**4**
Investment/(scrap)	11,000				(3,800)
Discount factor 8%	1	0.926	0.857	0.794	0.735
Present value	11,000	0	0	0	(2,793)
Net present cost	8,207				

(b)

Time	**0**	**1**	**2**	**3**	**4**
Lease payment	1,900	1,900	1,900	1,900	
Discount factor 8%	1	0.926	0.857	0.794	0.735
Present value	1,900	1,759	1,628	1,509	
Net present cost	6,796				

(c) Vans should be leased as this option has the lowest net present cost.

(d) Areas of risk include reliability of work carried out by the leasing company garage, waiting times and ability to cover area served by the firm. If, for instance, waiting times for repair increase then vehicles will be off the road for longer and either engineers would not be able to get to call-outs or standby vehicles will need to be made available.

If highly skilled staff are replaced by lower skilled staff and things do not progress well then it may not be easy to replace the staff. Other staff may feel threatened by the changes and this could affect staff motivation.

Task 5

(a)

Ratio	Year ended 31.12.20-4	Year ended 31.12.20-5
Return on capital employed	22.07%	23.48%
Gearing	11.85%	10.87%
Quick/acid test ratio	2.14:1	2.21:1
Inventory holding period	21 days	21 days
Working capital cycle	54 days	54 days

(b) **Profitability**

Revenue has grown by **11.11**%. The gross profit margin has decreased by **2.52**%. The cause of this difference is the low margins on some of the installations successfully tendered for.

The level of growth in the operating profit margin indicates **good** control over overheads.

Financial position

ABL continues to have **low** levels of gearing.

Liquidity

ABL has **high** levels of liquidity and could be considered to be **overcapitalised**.

Working capital management

The components of the working capital cycle are fairly constant. The trade receivables collection period has **improved** slightly and the trade payables payment period has **deteriorated** a little.

Overall performance

The **growth** in the return on capital employed indicates an overall **improvement** in performance.

Task 6

(a) Fuel purchasing system is robust making fraud difficult and costs easy to monitor. Engineers cannot use fuel cards to refuel own vehicles or buy additional items, breakdown on individual van mileage will highlight engineers using vans for own travel.

(b) One from:

Purchase order module

The lack of a purchase order system on Userve means that control over orders raised is weak. When an invoice is received at head office it is not possible to know that the goods were received on time or that they were of a suitable quality. All that can be checked is the price quoted on Userve. This could lead to ABL paying for parts which were faulty. In addition monitoring of costs accrued at any point in time will be difficult as there will not be any visibility of goods received and not invoiced. This will reduce the accuracy of figures in management accounts and reports. It will also make the monitoring of inventory held at branches more complex.

ABL should investigate the possibility of introducing job costing software at branches which have a purchase order module. If the firm wants to continue to use Userve, the firm may be able to commission a bespoke purchase order module which could be added to the current system.

Capital expenditure approval

Capital expenditure purchases frequently cost tens of thousands of pounds and significantly affect the operating efficiency and liquidity of a firm. ABL's systems only require the approval of one director for such orders. This could lead to problems if a director fails to take into account impacts of decisions on the firm as a whole.

ABL should introduce the requirement for approval by a second director of any large capital expenditure purchases, for instance, those over £5,000 in value.

(c) ABL could make use of its size by negotiating prices for heating and plumbing supplies centrally. At the moment branches negotiate prices individually, this will not be as effective because an individual branch has only a fraction of the buying power of the company. It may be possible to select a small number of preferred suppliers and gain improvements in both price and quality. However due to the large area covered by branches and the rural nature of the region the company may need to continue using several different suppliers.

(d) Microgeneration systems are a rapidly developing sector. Lack of specialist knowledge of individual Branch Managers and engineers with regard to developments in microgeneration technologies could lead to the installation of systems which are dated. Costs are continually being driven down in this sector and it is also likely that Branch Managers will not be able to keep up-to-date with the cost effectiveness of different systems. This may result in the firm losing customers and its current good reputation for work in this sector.

The purchasing of microgeneration systems should be managed by a specialist based at head office who can advise individual Branch Managers as required.

Answers to practice synoptic assessment 2

Task 1

(a) (a) Companies Act 2006

(d) Accounting standards

(b) (d) A good control environment

(c) (d) The Human Resources Director

(d)

Problem	Could have caused shortage	Would not cause shortage
(a) Miscoding of petty cash voucher as travel rather than subsistence		✔
(b) Theft of money from the petty cash tin	✔	
(c) Petty cash claims have been paid for more than the maximum amount allowed		✔
(d) Addition error on petty cash voucher		✔
(e) Clerical error paying out the wrong amount of petty cash	✔	

(e)

- Human error: **(e)** Sense checks which do not allow the posting of transactions with dates outside the current period
- Power failure: **(c)** Automatic back-ups

(f) Professional competence and due care

Task 2

(a) The budget used in the draft report is known as a fixed budget. This means that it was part of the originally agreed budget for the year and will have been approved by senior management. As such the budget represents the long term targets to which the firm should be working. These will tie in to the firm's long term strategy. The budget does not however help with cost control as the variances reported are largely caused by differences between the originally forecast level of activity and that which was achieved.

(b) The fixed budget is for a different volume of output to that which was achieved. This means that variances do not give us information about whether or not costs and revenues are in control. They just tell us whether or not the costs and revenues for the level of output achieved were more or less than for the original budgeted level.

The company could prepare a flexible budget. This would involve revising budgeted figures for variable costs and revenues to take account of the output level achieved. For example the budgeted revenue for sales of 3,000 tonnes was £1,275,000. If we revise this to take account of actual sales of 3,400 tonnes we arrive at a budgeted figure of £1,275,000 x 3,400/3,000 = £1,445,000. This tells us that had CDM forecast sales of 3,400 tonnes they would have forecast revenue of £27,000 more than was actually received. Which leads to an investigation of what had changed – did CDM reduce its selling prices and hence sell more tonnes, or did they sell a cheaper mix of products than expected? Analysing the flexed budget variance leads to a better understanding of operations.

Similarly, if we look at the forecast materials cost – this was £801,000 in the fixed budget. If we revise it for the volume change it becomes £801,000 x 3,400/3,000 = £907,800. This gives a favourable variance of £17,800. Materials costs were lower than would have been budgeted. Investigation should enable management to identify the causes and possibly take steps to consolidate such efficiencies.

As well as being useful in controlling costs and revenues, the flexed budget enables senior management to monitor the performance of departments and of managers. Middle managers, knowing that their performance will be monitored should be better motivated to work towards budgeted levels of efficiency.

(c) A standard costing system is one in which a planned, or standard cost is established for each item produced. Actual costs are monitored and compared to standard to identify variances – which can be analysed in more detail than variances from budget. For example, a materials variance can be split into the part caused by paying a different price for materials than planned and the part caused by using more or less materials than planned. Not only does this give greater insight into costs, it also helps to allocate responsibility for variances – the raw materials price variance is the responsibility of Buying, whereas the raw materials usage variance is the responsibility of Production. Standard costs can also be used to quickly produce draft budgets, and are useful in decision making calculations.

Standard costing systems are time consuming to set up, but for an organisation such as CDM which only makes a small range of products the benefits should outweigh the costs.

Task 3

Any five of the following:

Weakness	Potential problem for the company
Sales staff should check the status of an account before accepting an order – but if they are busy or only interested in achieving their sales targets then they may not do this. It is possible for an order to be placed even if an account is over its credit limit, or overdue or on stop	Sale to a bad credit risk, and subsequent irrecoverable debt
Human error is possible in the completion of the sales order worksheet – this could lead to orders being under-priced or over-priced. VAT might not be charged when due or could be charged on orders for which a zero rate applies	Errors in pricing or amounts of VAT could cause conflict with customers. If a lower price is quoted than due the company will probably have to honour this price even if the sale then becomes loss making
Human error could lead to some sales orders being missed and not emailed to production, or to some emails to production being delayed	Customers will be dissatisfied if goods are not received or received late and they could change to other suppliers. Production will find it harder to schedule output effectively if orders are not notified promptly
No despatch notes produced for customers to sign – customers could deny having received the goods	CDM will not be able to bring successful legal action against the customer in the event of the customer refusing to pay
Details of some despatches might not be emailed to the Sales Ledger Clerk, or there may be some delay in emailing details of the despatches	Sales might not be invoiced, causing loss to the company. Sales might be invoiced late – this will affect cash flow as payments will be made based on invoice date
The Sales Ledger Clerk is responsible for creating all invoices and credit notes	If the clerk were acting in collusion with a customer invoices could simply not be raised. Alternatively the clerk could issue credit notes to cancel off amounts outstanding in return for back-handers from customers

Task 4

(1) (a)

Year	0	1	2	3	4
Cash flow		265,000	238,500	214,650	793,185
Discount factor (10%)	1	0.909	0.826	0.751	0.683
Present value		240,885	197,001	161,202	541,745
Net present value	1,140,833				

Workings: Cash flow

Year 1: £275,000 + £50,000 – £60,000 = £265,000

Year 2: £265,000 x 90% = £238,500

Year 3: £238,500 x 90% = £214,650

Year 4: £214,650 x 90% = £193,185 + £800,000 – £120,000 – £80,000 = £793,185

(b) Site should be retained. Proceeds now £800,000 – £120,000 – £80,000 = £600,000. This is less than the net present value of retaining the site and selling it after four years.

(c) Operational risk at Lincolnshire if working to full capacity – no scope for breakdowns etc.

Social sustainability – skilled job losses resulting from closure in Southampton. Unlikely to be compensated for by low skilled holiday park employments.

(2) (a) Grade B should be cut back because contribution/tonne is lower (£45 for grade A, £40 for grade B)

(b) Use up inventories of finished goods

Transfer production to Lincolnshire

Contact customers to see if they can accept delayed supplies

(3) (a) £300 x 78% = £234

(b) Raw materials cost/tonne malt extract = £140/0.7 = £200

Target other manufacturing cost = £234 – £200 = £34

Task 5

(a)

Ratio	Year ended 30.12.20-5	Year ended 30.12.20-6
Operating profit margin %	7.84%	9.07%
Interest cover	2.29 times	1.76 times
Gearing	35.59%	59.98%
Current ratio	1.43:1	1.57:1
Trade payables payment period	123 days	112 days
Working capital cycle*	40 days	52 days

*working capital cycle not asked for, but needs to be calculated to answer the question on working capital management.

(b) **Profitability**

(c) The improvement in the gross profit margin and the operating profit margin could not have been achieved if costs had increased in line with revenue

Financial position

(c) The company has gone from having medium levels of gearing to high levels of gearing

Liquidity

(a) Both liquidity ratios have improved over the year

Working capital management

(c) The change in the trade payables payment period indicates a lack of financial control

Overall performance

(b) Although underlying profitability has improved in 20-6, the level of gearing and resultant interest costs are a significant cause for concern

Task 6

(a) **Payment systems** – Payments are made by BACS – this is efficient and cost effective. The payment system is well controlled with good segregation of duties resulting in a low risk of fraud in the payment system. Checks on cash flow should ensure that payments are only made when the company has funds available to honour the payment. The use of emails to confirm payments is a sustainable method of communicating and keeps stationery and postage costs down.

(b) One from:

IT systems

- IT systems – there are lots of gaps in control which make systems time consuming for staff, prone to human error and open to fraud. For instance buyers need to physically check grain invoices against agreements with suppliers, hard copies of weighbridge records and sample test results – this is very time consuming. Similarly the Purchase Ledger Clerk needs to manually input Invoice details, this is very slow and prone to human error. In addition lots of controls over authorisation could be circumvented by the Purchase Ledger Clerk. Were the Purchase Ledger Clerk acting in collusion with a supplier, fictitious invoices, or invoices with inflated prices could be input to the system.
- The new IT systems which have purchase order processing should be able to address these issues. For instance weighbridge records would be automatically recorded on the system and show on the relevant farmers' account for the Buyers to see. Purchase invoices could be scanned and uploaded and controls enforced - purchase orders will be put on the system by originators only and invoices will not be able to be processed without being matched to these purchase orders.

Grain purchases

- Decisions about the quantities of grains to be purchased are made by two directors based on market experience. The decisions are made shortly before the plans need to be put into action. If the directors fail to take changes into account or if the buyers do not react quickly enough the company may buy too much or too little grain and may not pay the best prices.
- Outline plans should be made available earlier in the year so that buyers have time to plan the most effective way of achieving expected targets rather than to simply "do their best" to achieve these targets. More use should be made of analysis of trends and of market research to ensure that targets are properly thought out.

(c) One of:

- Expand the scheme of agreeing three year contracts with farmers – this improves quality and reduces uncertainty. More certainty about product costs would enable better decisions to be made about selling prices.
- The new IT systems could be discussed as an opportunity (as discussed in (b) above).

(d) The level of gearing of the firm is high and CDM has swings in its liquidity over the year caused by the seasonal nature of its business. Should interest rates rise significantly the firm would be in a very vulnerable position. Careful attention must be paid to the management of liquidity and to a reduction in the level of gearing for the long-term survival of the firm to be assured.

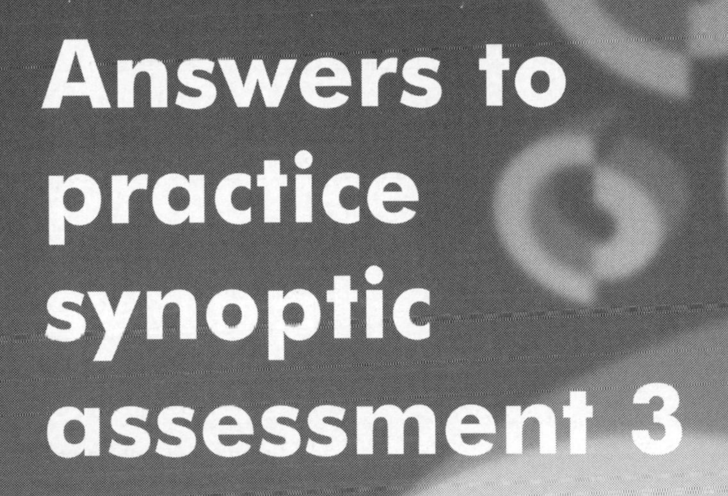

Answers to practice synoptic assessment 3

Task 1

(a)

	Lenders	Credit customers	Management
To assess potential for future growth		✔	
To assess security for borrowings	✔		
To assess potential for future dividend payments			

(b) (c) Advise the Assistant Accountant of the error so that it can be rectified

(c)

Problem	Could have caused shortage	Would not cause shortage
(a) Receipt of goods incorrectly keyed in as 100 units instead of 1,000 units		✔
(b) Theft of stores	✔	
(c) Issue of stores to production incorrectly keyed in as 100 units instead of 1,000 units.	✔	
(d) A container of goods on the production line was counted twice.		✔
(e) Stock records not updated for disposal of out-of-date inventory.	✔	

(d) (b) Accounting system will not accept transactions with a future date

(e) Credit notes need to be raised by a clerk and checked by the Financial Accountant before they are passed for posting

(e) Integrity

(f) True

Task 2

(a) A 'Top-down' budgetary system is one where senior managers produce the budgets which are set for junior managers to work towards. FBL use top-down budgeting. This is an advantage in that shop managers are unlikely to have the skills to be able to analyse trends and make accurate forecasts – unlike the Management Accountant. So budgets can be relied on to take into account trends in sales of different products as well as inflation and company strategy.

(b) A 'Participative' budgetary system is one in which junior managers are involved in the process of setting their own budgets. Junior managers will always have more detailed knowledge of their specific department – in FBL's case of their individual shop, than senior managers. By involving shop managers FBL would be able to include this detailed knowledge in their plans making them more accurate. Shop managers may also feel more motivated to try to achieve their budgetary targets if they have been involved in developing them.

(c) A flexed budget is a budget which has been revised to reflect the level of activity which has actually been achieved. This means that budgeted variable costs will have been revised to show the amounts that would have been budgeted had the activity level been known in advance. As a result of this all variances purely relate to costs and revenues which are at a level higher or lower than that which would have been expected. These over or underspends can be investigated and appropriate control action taken.

(d) Raw Material price variance £ (249) (adverse)

((1,660kg x £2) – £3,569))

Raw material usage variance £ (44) (adverse)

((5,460 x 0.3kg x £2) – (1,660kg x £2))

(e) A flexed budget allows us to see whether more or less has been spent on raw materials than budgeted for the level of output achieved, but it does not tell us what caused the variance. Standard costing analysis allows us to see that £249 of the overspend was caused by the firm paying more for its raw materials than standard and £44 was caused by the firm using more materials than standard. This will help to control costs as the Buying Department are responsible for negotiating prices so can be held to account for the price variance, whereas the Production Department are responsible for the usage variance.

Task 3

Five of the following:

Weakness	Potential problem for the company
Customers are not credit checked in any way before accounts are opened	Sale to a bad credit risk and subsequent irrecoverable debt
No formal credit agreements are produced for signature by the customer before trading commences	Lack of clarity over terms of trade. Possible problems should disputes arise and need to be resolved in court
Staff do not check the status of an account before accepting an order.	Sale to a bad credit risk, and subsequent irrecoverable debt
No debt collection policy	Staff will take an ad hoc approach if problems arise. Staff have no guidance about what they should be doing and when the action should be taken
No member of staff responsible for monitoring customer accounts and chasing debts	Problems will remain undetected for a long time. Customers who delay payment will not be held to account. This may encourage late payments by customers who could afford to pay but want to maximise their own cash flow
No procedures for chasing accounts or for putting customers' accounts on stop	Problems will be identified through review of the management accounts – but these are only produced at month end and so problems could have become quite serious before they are picked up – and additional sales may well have been made to customers with liquidity problems. This will affect the liquidity of FBL and, should debts go bad, their profitability
Invoices and statements are posted to customers	This is expensive and slow compared with emailing these documents. It is also not environmentally friendly
No agreed credit limits	No limit on potential bad debt risk

Task 4

(a) £180,000 ÷ 90 = **£2,000** per recipe.

(b) £2,000 ÷ 24 days ÷ 1,000 litres x 100p = **8.33** pence per litre of soup.

(c) £2,000 ÷ 300days ÷ 7,000 x 100p = **0.10** pence per sausage roll.

(d) A large chunk of the cost of a product is made up of the overheads allocated to it. Activity based costing will give FBL more accurate overhead costs and so more accurate product costs. This means decisions about the selling prices and profitability of different products will be based on more accurate information, loss making products will be clearly identified and decisions can be made either to discontinue them or to increase their selling prices.

(e) Facility costs are costs such as site security or site maintenance. These costs can not be allocated to products on the basis of activities – instead they will always need to be allocated and apportioned as they are with absorption costing, so both systems will apportion facility costs in the same way.

(f) Normal accounting systems monitor profitability on a monthly, quarterly or annual basis. Product life cycle costing is different because it attempts to review all the costs and revenues associated with a product or piece of machinery over the whole of its life. This is useful because the profitability of a product can vary depending on whether it has just been launched, or is in its' growth stage or has reached maturity or decline. By reviewing the whole of the product's life cycle when making decisions about product R&D and launch, the firm is able to take this variability into account in advance and make better decisions. Similarly, by reviewing not just the purchase price of equipment, but also the savings it will generate over time as well as future maintenance costs and scrap values, capital expenditure decisions will be based on higher quality information.

Task 5

(a)

Ratio	**Company overall**	**High Street Shop**	**New out of town shop**
Profitability			
Gross profit margin %	38%	34.96%	39.13%
Operating profit margin %	2.91%	1.03%	5.22%
Asset turnover	4.63 times	7.48 times	2.21 times
Return on capital employed	13.47%	7.69%	11.54%*
Inventory holding period	16 days	12 days	8 days

*new store has only been open for 6 months, full year's return = 2 x 12 = 24, ROCE 24/208 x100 = 11.54%

(b)

1. Profit margins at **the high street shop** give cause for concern.
2. Operating profit margins indicate that overheads make up a **similar** proportion of revenue at the 2 shops.
3. Relative to the assets invested, **both shops** are operating at levels of profitability lower than the company average.
4. A new shop will go through its own product life cycle and at the growth stage would be expected to have **medium** levels of profitability.
5. The return on capital employed of the long established high street shop may be **inflated** if non-current assets have not been revalued.
6. The asset turnover of the new out of town shop may be **depressed** because of the value of recently purchased land and buildings.
7. The benchmark return on capital employed for similar businesses is 20%. If FBL want to move closer to this level of return they need to consider closing stores such as **the high street shop**.
8. Inventory holding periods at both stores are better than the company average which is probably due to **the fact that the majority of inventories are kept at the factory**.
9. Management are **likely** to be concerned about the performance of the high street shop.
10. Management are **not likely** to be concerned about the performance of the new out of town shop.

Task 6

(a) One from:

- Accounting software package used is efficient and ensures compliance with RTI requirements. Changes to tax rates and allowances are adjusted through automatic updates so FBL can be sure that the right amounts of taxes are being charged and paid to the government.
- The segregation of duties between HR who set–up and remove employees on the payroll system and the Payroll Clerk who records the hours worked, reduces the risk of fraud. A fictitious employee could not be paid unless there was collusion between HR and the Payroll Clerk – making this type of fraud much more unlikely.
- The payment of wages by BACS is secure and cost effective in that it is far less time consuming to administer than payments by cash or cheques and the risk of theft or fraud is a lot lower. In addition bank charges for automated payments are lower than for cash or cheque payments.

(b) One from:

- Reliance on shop managers for identifying optimum staffing level for shop – could result in overstaffing or understaffing. This could frustrate shop workers and antagonise customers.
- Reliance on shop managers transferring clocking data to USB and emailing to Payroll Clerk – time consuming and risk of loss of data.
- Staff could swipe friends' smartcards and make it look as if they arrived or left work earlier or later than actually occurred. This would increase the wages costs of the company.
- Managers are responsible for notifying HR of leavers. They could collude with staff who have left, not report their leaving and continue to clock them in and out to defraud the company.

(c) One from:

- FBL could invest in a workforce management system which would help to identify the best staffing levels for each shop and the most economic shift patterns. This would improve the control of shop workers' wages.
- FBL could upgrade clocking system to use biometric data such as facial recognition or fingerprints. This would eliminate the risk of employees clocking in or out for each other.
- FBL could upgrade the clocking systems so that data is transferred directly to the Payroll Clerk without shop managers needing to download or upload the data. This would save shop manager time, get the information to the Payroll Clerk more quickly and reduce the risks of data loss or corruption.

(d) FBL could be at risk of legal proceedings if shop managers fail to properly carry out checks – such as that a prospective worker has the right to work in the UK – or if they breach some other aspect of employment law such as the Equalities Act or the Working Time Directive. Legal proceedings would be expensive and would damage the reputation of the business. FBL needs to ensure that all shop managers receive adequate HR training before interviewing any prospective employees.

Answers to practice synoptic assessment 4

Task 1

(a) **(a)** and **(c)** Purchasing team; **(b)** and **(d)** Accounts Department

(b) (b) It's appropriate for the Accounts Payable Clerk to help if s/he has time available as the work should contribute to the solvency and cost effectiveness of the firm – these are key factors which the Accounts Department tries to control

(c) **(a)** and **(b)** are false; **(c)** is true

(d) **(a)** and **(b)** would be detected; **(c)** would not

(e) Automatic back-ups of data are made every time a user posts a transaction: **(a)**

User profiles restrict staff access to the accounting system so that only authorised tasks can be performed: **(b)**

(f) **(1)** confidentiality; **(2)** yes; **(3)** no

Task 2

(a) The budgets will:

- ensure that senior management have a clearly thought out plan of action for the future and have assessed its viability
- give managers a target to work towards. People are motivated by having goals and a budget which is challenging, but achievable, will motivate managers to work hard to achieve their targets
- help to co-ordinate the different departments in the firm as all will be planning for the same level of activity. The impacts on support departments, such as the accounts department, of operational activities can be identified and planned for. So, for example, the impacts on cash flow of planned purchases and sales can be identified
- identify authorised capital expenditure and communicate this clearly to departments and staff
- give the company a benchmark against which actual results can be measured and which will help to identify improvements which can be made to the firm's operations

(b)

Products	**20-7 Sales Units**	**20-7 Budget materials and components cost** *£000*
Vehicles	222	8,355
Recycling banks	190	397
Maintenance and services	1,668	698
	Total	**9,450**

(c) Materials usage/unit of output

Materials wastage %

Steel price/metre

Raw material price and usage variances

Task 3

Weakness	**Potential problem for the company**
Purchasing systems and procedures are not documented	This could lead to problems in the event of staff changes or illness. New staff or those working as cover might not be able to operate efficiently and could make costly mistakes – such as approving invoices which are overcharging for goods or for which no goods have been received
The Accounts Payable Clerk is responsible for creating supplier accounts, recording invoices and reconciling supplier statements	The Accounts Payable Clerk could commit fraud against the company by creating bogus suppliers and recording fictitious invoices from them. Alternatively the clerk could work in collusion with a genuine supplier to record invoices for which goods have never been received
The Accounts Payable Clerk is responsible for entering all supplier details	The accounts payable clerk could change supplier bank details to a bank account which s/he controls
Credit card statements are only checked back to receipts - the validity of receipts is not checked. There is no check of fuel usage or mileage against the location of jobs	Field engineers could be using credit cards to pay for fuel for their own vehicles or other personal expenses. As their costs are charged to jobs, this will make EGP's charges to customers more expensive and could lead to EGP losing contracts
There are delays in recording purchase invoices received if all details do not match exactly with purchase orders and goods received records	Payments could be made late. This would lose supplier goodwill and reduce any chance of gaining prompt payment discounts. Monthly management accounts might be inaccurate as these invoices cannot be automatically accrued for, manual accruals are slow work
Remittance advices are posted to suppliers	This is slow, expensive (in terms of postage and stationery costs) and not good for the environment as it uses up lots of paper
Blank cheques are stored in a desk	The cheques could easily be stolen and used to commit fraud against the company

Task 4

Part 1

(a) IT system upgrade £2,400

(b) An opportunity cost is the benefit you could have achieved by taking an alternative course of action. For example, if you are offered an extra day's work on a Saturday for £100, but choose to visit family instead, the opportunity cost of visiting family is £100.

(c) The opportunity cost of training the Accounts Payable Clerk will be the value of the work which s/he could have completed if not being trained. Since the Accounts Payable Clerk is paid £8 per hour, the value of work done must be £8 per hour. This means that the opportunity cost of the training is 3 hours x £8 per hour, equals £24, plus employer costs of 14%, equals £27.36.

(d) Saved stationery – no need to print invoices sent in as pdfs.

Saved staff time – no need to print invoices sent in as pdfs.

Saved toner cartridges – no need to print invoices sent in as pdfs.

Saved filing and storage costs – reduction in the number of files being used and of storage boxes.

If invoice storage is external – costs will be saved – storage boxes do not need to be stored for six years.

Staff time saved – retrieval of old invoices is no longer time consuming.

(e) Staff may feel stressed by the changeover, job satisfaction might suffer whilst staff get used to new procedures. This could lead to increased levels of staff sickness.

Staff may struggle to work with normal efficiency whilst learning the new systems which could delay work or increase the level of overtime worked by accounts staff.

(f) Improved relationships with suppliers as invoices are more likely to be paid on time.

Space will be freed up if invoices had been stored internally.

Improved staff morale as less time will be spent searching for invoices either in the files on "unmatched" invoices or in the files of approved invoices or in the invoice archive.

Improved accuracy of accruals in monthly management accounts will improve the quality of management information allowing for better decision making and planning.

Part 2

	Council 5	**Council 8**	**Council 17**
Contribution from order (£s)	476	196	294
Contribution per hour (£s)	11.90	14	12.25
Hours allocated to job	10	14	24

Task 5

(a)

Ratio	Year ended 30.6.20-5	Year ended 30.6.20-6
Return on capital employed	17.6%	12.69%
Gearing (debt/equity)	59.07%	75.98%
Quick/acid test ratio	1.68:1	1.59:1
Trade receivables collection period	47 days	49 days
Working capital cycle	68 days	74. days

(b) **Profitability**

(b) The fall in the operating profit margin is caused both by the reduction in the gross profit margin and by the increase in operating expenses as a proportion of revenue

Financial position

(c) Casper Components Ltd has medium levels of gearing

Liquidity

(a) Casper Components Ltd current ratios could indicate that it is holding too many current assets

Working capital management

(a) The changes to all the working capital ratios could result from overtrading

Summary

(b) EGP should consider investing in Casper Components Ltd as it generates returns higher than EGP does

Task 6

(a) One from:

- Expertise of the sales team – enables the company to compete successfully in a complex marketplace.
- Credit checks used and terms of trade agreed for customers along with retention of title clauses and signed despatch notes – procedures reduce the risks of sales to bad credit risks, sales contracts which are unenforceable in court and losses due to bad debts.

(b) One from:

- No involvement of accounts team in checking the profitability of prospective bids to clients – could result in bids being made which are unprofitable. The accounts team should have some input at the bid stage, ideally bids should be costed using standard accounting software.
- Engineers recording job costs manually and then sending record to the office for input after a delay is slow and a duplication of work. The manual record could cause errors in data input as the engineer's handwriting might not be easy to read. Invoices may well go out over a week after the initial service was performed resulting in over a week's delay in the eventual receipt as dates of payment are based on invoiced dates, not the date that the service was carried out. EGP should investigate the option of giving engineers laptops which would

enable them to log on to EGPs systems remotely and upload job costs onto EGP systems in real time.

- Sending invoices out in the post is slow "snailmail" and expensive in terms of stationery and postage costs, as well as requiring staff time to fold invoices and put them into envelopes. EGP should investigate whether or not invoices can be emailed to customers.

(c) One from:

- Sales of maintenance and services are not currently marketed – they are sold on the back of the sales of refuse vehicles only. Given the stresses in the market place it might be possible to grow this area of the business by advertising it on the company's website and tendering to service vehicles from other manufacturers.
- The sales team could monitor vehicles sold and their maintenance costs to establish the point at which they are no longer economic to maintain. At this point they should contact customers and invite them to discuss the costs of continuing to maintain equipment compared with the costs of buying new equipment. Possible purchase options should be explored with these customers.

(d) One from:

- Should the Sales Director retire, EGP may not have the expertise necessary to successfully complete bids for council work. The Sales Director works on the detail of each bid and junior staff may not have developed enough of an oversight of the process to be able to replace Gloria seamlessly.
- Economic factors such as further austerity measures resulting in local authority cutbacks reducing demand and sales, falls in the value of sterling putting up prices of raw materials and reducing profit margins or a reduction in subsidies for investment in recycling cutting demand.

for your notes

for your notes

for your notes

for your notes

for your notes

for your notes

for your notes

for your notes

for your notes

for your notes